STURM

STURM

Ernst Jünger

Translated by Alexis P. Walker

Edited and with an Introduction by David Pan

Telos Press Publishing
Candor, NY

Printed in the United States of America

19   18   17   16   15   1   2   3   4

Translated by permission from the German original, *Sturm*, in Ernst Jünger, *Sämtliche Werke*, vol. 15, pp. 9–74, Stuttgart 1978. © 1923, 1965, 1978 Klett-Cotta—J. G. Cotta'sche Buchhandlung Nachfolger GmbH, Stuttgart.

Translation copyright © 2015 Alexis P. Walker

ISBN: 978-0-914386-54-4

Library of Congress Cataloging-in-Publication Data

Jünger, Ernst, 1895–1998, author.
 [Sturm. English]
 Sturm / Ernst Junger ; Translated by Alexis P. Walker ; Edited and with an Introduction by David Pan.
    pages cm
 Summary: Set in 1916 in the days before the Somme offensive, Ernst Jünger's Sturm provides a vivid portrait of the front-line experiences of four German infantry officers and their company. A highly cultivated man and an acute observer of his era, the eponymous Lieutenant Sturm entertains his friends during lulls in the action with readings from his literary sketches. The text's forays into philosophical and social commentary address many of the themes of Jünger's early work, such as the nature of war, death, heroism, the phenomenon of Rausch, and mass society—Provided by publisher
 ISBN 978-0-914386-54-4 (pbk.)
 1. World War, 1914–1918—Fiction. 2. Germany. Heer—Fiction. 3. Soldiers—Fiction. I. Walker, Alexis P., translator. II. Pan, David, 1963– editor. III. Title.
 PT2619.U43S8613 2015
 833'.912—dc23

2015024804

Cover design by Amanda Trager and Erik Moskowitz

Telos Press Publishing
PO Box 811
Candor, NY 13743
www.telospress.com

Contents

Translator's Preface

Alexis P. Walker

I was first attracted to Ernst Jünger's work by the swirl of controversy surrounding it. Assigned to read *On the Marble Cliffs* for an undergraduate literature class, I understood that Jünger was an almost-but-not-quite Nazi—yet the work itself was a not-so-veiled critique of totalitarianism. Critical and biographical accounts did little to allay my confusion: He was a son of the middle class with pronounced aristocratic, anti-bourgeois leanings; a highly decorated soldier who had a decidedly ambivalent, not to say self-contradictory, view of modern technological warfare; a "fellow traveler" during the Nazi regime, in the eyes of many, who resigned his membership in his World War I regiment's veterans organization in the early 1930s when its Jewish members were expelled. Even stranger was the fact that, according to various sources, both Adolf Hitler and Bertolt Brecht(!) answered complaints about him with virtually the same response: "Don't bother me about Jünger—he has many merits." Of course, the merits they had in mind were quite different. According to stage designer Teo Otto, at least, the source of Brecht's (perhaps grudging?) approval was quite specific: "I admire and respect his German."[1]

This last remark proved irresistible to a student already fascinated by language and in particular by the art of translation, thanks in large part to an earlier reading of Walter Benjamin's

1. As quoted in Walter Hinck, "Sternhagelvoll am Kreuzweg: Carl Zuckmayer und sein Verhältnis zu Brecht und Jünger," *Frankfurter Allgemeine Zeitung*, October 1, 1999, p. 42.

brilliant essay "The Task of the Translator." What prose style was powerful enough to induce Brecht to overlook an ideology so seemingly at odds with his own? Would I know it when I read it? Most importantly, would it translate?

Exploration of this question led me to attempt a translation of the novella you have now in your hands. Originally published in installments in the *Hannoverscher Kurier* in 1923, *Sturm* was either forgotten or ignored by Jünger until 1960, when it was rediscovered by Hans Peter des Coudres, one of Jünger's bibliographers. Des Coudres republished it in a limited edition in 1963, and it was included subsequently in Jünger's collected works, which is where I encountered it several decades later.

Relatively short and action-packed—and, not inconsequentially, previously untranslated—*Sturm* seemed like the perfect material for my first real foray into translation. The task almost immediately proved more difficult than I'd expected. As a young woman with limited exposure to military history, I soon encountered obstacles in the form of World War I–era military terminology: Terms like *Niemandsland* translated neatly into the familiar English "no-man's-land," but how to accurately translate terms like *Stollentreppen,* which referred to a feature of German-built trenches I couldn't clearly picture and couldn't find reflected in the trench diagrams I consulted?[2] Jünger's deep interest in zoology, botany, and entomology (which he pursued professionally after the war) presented challenges of a different sort: Would the technically correct common name "scarce copper" be the best translation for *Dukatenfalter* (*Lycaena virgaureae*), or would its obscurity introduce confusion? In

---

2. I eventually settled on the mining term "galleries" as a translation for *Stollen*—horizontal, deeply dug tunnels that were distinct from dugouts but similarly used for the protection of soldiers. (Such deep construction was more characteristic of German trenches than of English trenches—hence, I believe, my difficulty in finding a decent English translation.)

general, wherever possible, I preferred using words etymologically related to the original, or at least from the same register. How, though, to avoid the imprecision of "white butterflies," the only common English name I could find for *die Weißlinge* (*Pieridae*), a vast family including butterflies of many colors?[3] Virtually every page presented questions like these.

As I continued to work, I came under the spell of Jünger's prose, and solving these isolated puzzles in translation, while still fascinating, began to seem far less difficult than doing justice to that prose's intensity and controlled beauty. *Sturm* brings vividly to life the worlds of the trenches and of city life in Germany, as seen through the eyes of an intellectual-turned-war-hero, the eponymous Sturm ("storm," in English). The text's practical, intellectual, and philosophical concerns place it firmly in the era of the First World War, but—cliché or not—the voice of the narrator belongs to every era and no era. Capturing this voice and approximating the effect of immediacy it has in the original seemed ultimately a far greater challenge than finding in every instance *le mot juste.*

Through many, many revisions, I nevertheless did my best on both fronts, and submitted the finished translation of *Sturm* as part of my senior thesis at Yale. Afterward, life happened, in its varied forms. I never forgot passages from the novella, though, and often held up fragments of Jünger's descriptions— a suit that "played in two soft tones of nutmeg brown"; the "mosaic of brown, red, and yellow leaves" spread on the flagstones of a city in autumn—against my own observations of New York.

Recently, I dusted the text off to see what new insights the intervening years might have brought. The ruminative passages now struck me as more plentiful and possibly more turgid

3. The decisions I made on these two particular questions—often reversed, and always open to debate—were "yes" and "it's *not* possible," respectively.

than I had remembered (perhaps reflective of my middle-aged, bourgeois discomfort with the author's anti-liberal tendencies?). I nevertheless found myself as fully immersed in the narrative as I was the first time. I decided to rewrite my translation, altering and refining it in order as much as possible to thin the veil that translation interposes between the original and its reader. I did additional research (for which the Internet, of course, proved invaluable) to add precision to terms that had presented difficulties the first time around. Most importantly, however, I tried once again in every sentence to reproduce the rhythm and structure of Jünger's prose so that it would read as naturally in English as it does in the original German. An impossible task, of course, but one worth pursuing.

I hope that your experience reading the text is as enjoyable and productive as my experience translating—and re-translating—it has been.

Introduction

David Pan

In his 1915 "Thoughts for the Times on War and Death," Sigmund Freud begins by describing the disillusionment with the advance of civilization brought about by the horrors of World War I, in which it became clear that "the great world-dominating nations of white race upon whom the leadership of the human species had fallen" had neither been able to avoid war through rational discussion nor to tame the barbarity of war through the restrictions of international law.[1] Indeed, this particular war only brought home the incredible brutality of a war that had at its disposal all the technological capabilities of modern society. In considering this disillusionment, he concludes that civilized man is in fact not so different from "primaeval man," and that war "strips us of the later accretions of civilization, and lays bare the primal man in each of us."[2] For Freud, civilization sets up a set of restrictions on human instinctual violence, but these restrictions fall away once people are given the opportunity to live out this otherwise hidden desire for murder and violence. War becomes a kind of primal force that breaks through the superficial crust of culture. Freud concludes that "war cannot be abolished; so long as the conditions of existence among nations are so different and their mutual repulsion so violent, there are bound to be wars. The question

1. Sigmund Freud, "Thoughts for the Times on War and Death," in *Standard Edition of the Complete Psychological Works of Sigmund Freud*, ed. James Strachey, Anna Freud, et al. (London: Hogarth, 1953–74), vol. 14, p. 276.
2. Ibid., p. 299.

then arises: Is it not we who should give in, who should adapt ourselves to war? Should we not confess that in our civilized attitude towards death we are once again living psychologically beyond our means, and should we not rather turn back and recognize the truth? Would it not be better to give death the place in reality and in our thoughts which is its due, and to give a little more prominence to the unconscious attitude towards death which we have hitherto so carefully suppressed?"[3] If there were any question about the bleakness of this stance, Freud goes on in the next lines to end his essay with the chilling words: "*Si vis vitam, para mortem.* If you want to endure life, prepare yourself for death."[4]

This call to embrace death as an essential part of life is the starting point for the writing of Ernst Jünger, whose life-long reflections on the relation between violence and culture originate in his descriptions of his experience as a soldier in the trenches of World War I. Contrary to Freud, though, he did not feel disillusionment with the outbreak of World War I, but excitement. Indeed, even before the war, he had run away from home to join the French Foreign Legion in Africa in order to taste the danger of war when it was still confined to the colonies. The restlessness that motivated Jünger's enthusiastic participation in war comes of a raising of the stakes for life that Freud was equally willing to accept as a reality of war: "Life is impoverished, it loses in interest, when the highest stake in the game of living, life itself, may not be risked. It becomes as shallow and empty as, let us say, an American flirtation, in which it is understood from the first that nothing is to happen, as contrasted with a Continental love-affair in which both partners must bear its serious consequences in mind."[5] By contrast, it is

3. Ibid.
4. Ibid., p. 300.
5. Ibid., p. 290.

only in war that "[l]ife has, indeed, become interesting again; it has recovered its full content."[6] As Karl Heinz Bohrer has argued,[7] Freud's affirmation of the meaningfulness of life in the context of war points to a more than passing affinity with Jünger's more open affirmation of violence. Even the metaphor of the love affair is not an idle one, as Jünger also takes it up in a much more serious way in his attempts to make sense of the violence of the war experience. But if Freud continues to use in his later writings the same schema of a direct opposition between the violence of war as an instinct and the strictures of culture that suppress this instinct,[8] Jünger's intense engagement with the war experience leads him to a variety of different and ultimately more nuanced perspectives on the relation between violence and culture.

Previous English translations of Jünger's work by Telos Press have in fact traced his varied attempts to understand this relationship. The first, *On Pain*, originally published in 1934, describes a modern situation in which the individual has become integrated within a state apparatus. As Russell Berman points out in the preface, "Jünger describes the reduction of the personality through a thorough instrumentalization, a transformation of the formerly heroic warrior into a merely technical component in a way that dooms the soldier to a living

6. Ibid., p. 291.

7. Karl Heinz Bohrer, *Die Ästhetik des Schreckens: Die pessimistische Romantik und Ernst Jüngers Frühwerk* (Munich: Carl Hanser, 1978), pp. 85–87.

8. Freud repeats this schema for understanding the violence of war as an outbreak of instinctual aggression in *Civilization and Its Discontents*, where he argues that the development of civilization does not necessarily lead to a reduction of aggressive instincts. Rather, "[i]n consequence of this primary mutual hostility of human beings, civilized society is perpetually threatened with disintegration." Sigmund Freud, *Civilization and Its Discontents*, in *Standard Edition of the Complete Psychological Works of Sigmund Freud*, ed. James Strachey, Anna Freud, et al. (London: Hogarth, 1953–74), vol. 21, p. 112.

death."⁹ As Berman describes, Jünger's hardened affirmation of this instrumentalization of the individual to the state's total mobilization of society links his work not only to the rise of Nazism but to the suicide bombings and beheadings of today's new totalitarian movements. Later, with his own disillusionment, not with World War I but with the Nazi movement, Jünger turns more inward, and in the 1938 edition of *The Adventurous Heart*, published in English by Telos Press in 2012, Jünger retreats from political positions and pronouncements. He offers instead, according to Eliah Bures and Elliot Neaman, "a detached view, eavesdropping on life, to be sure, but without the customary emotional or moral commitments that might jeopardize the knowledge obtained from such a distance."¹⁰ The link between *On Pain*'s integration of the individual to the needs of the state and the detached attitude of *The Adventurous Heart* lies in the sovereign attitude of the individual, creating a kind of indifference toward violence in both cases. This sovereignty of the individual is also the attitude that motivates *The Forest Passage* of 1951 (in English with Telos Press in 2013), in which Jünger describes rebellion against a totalitarian system as an affirmation of freedom, even if such acts of resistance lead to the death of the actor. While these three texts provide some insight into the development of Jünger's work in the Nazi period and its aftermath, they are also puzzling when taken together, as they seem to directly contradict each other. While the earlier and later works all feature a striving for an indifference to violence that serves the development of individual courage, there is also a jarring disconnect between *On Pain*'s affirmation of

9. Russell A. Berman, "Preface," in Ernst Jünger, *On Pain*, trans. David C. Durst (New York: Telos Press Publishing, 2008), p. xvi.

10. Eliah Bures and Elliot Neaman, "Introduction," in Ernst Jünger, *The Adventurous Heart: Figures and Capriccios*, 2nd ed., ed. Russell A. Berman, trans. Thomas Friese (Candor, NY: Telos Press Publishing, 2012), p. xli.

"a breed of resolute men obedient to authority,"[11] on the one hand, and *The Forest Passage*'s invocation of "the forest rebel's determination to resist," on the other.[12] Is this turnaround with respect to obedience and resistance simply a result of Jünger's disillusionment with the Nazis, or is there some fundamental contradiction in Jünger's work and thought that would lead to these opposing attitudes toward Nazism and its violence?

As I would like to lay out, much of the answer can be derived from a closer look at Jünger's early war writings, and in particular *Sturm*, deftly translated here by Alexis Walker. While some writers of World War I, such as Erich Maria Remarque and Wilfred Owen, recounted the horrors of the war in order to lay out a pacificist stance, others, including Hitler and the Nazis, used the war to develop a nationalist perspective. Much of Jünger's political writing falls within this latter category, yet the descriptions of the war for which he became famous, *Storms of Steel* (1920) and *Battle as Inner Experience* (1922), are perhaps closest to Expressionist literature, which turns war into a kind of mythic force in poems such as Georg Heym's "The War" and Georg Trakl's "Grodek." These writers describe the war as a force of nature, regarding war from the point of view of spectators of a kind of aesthetics of horror. Jünger does something similar, but lays out a unique perspective by portraying the horrors of war, not just with images of "the god of war" like the Expressionists, but directly and dispassionately in such a way as to arrive at the image of a new sovereignty of the individual in the face of the violence of war. But if the war experience establishes the issues of violence, pain, and courage as the key themes that motivate his writing, his work includes a variety of approaches to the problem, as if each text were a fresh

11. Jünger, *On Pain*, p. 18.

12. Ernst Jünger, *The Forest Passage*, ed. Russell A. Berman, trans. Thomas Friese (Candor, NY: Telos Press Publishing, 2013), p. 25.

take on the problem, resulting in texts that vary to the point of contradiction.

This experimentation led to the particular situation of the story *Sturm*, which was for a long time a "lost" text. Even though he made his reputation as a writer with a series of texts about his experiences in World War I, this particular story was not recognized as part of this war writing. The story was originally published serially from April 11–27, 1923, in sixteen issues of the newspaper *Hannoverscher Kurier: Zeitung für Norddeutschland*. After that, Jünger claims to have forgotten about the text, and there was no mention of this work by any commentators or critics until it was discovered by the Jünger bibliographer Hans Peter des Coudres, who published it for the first time in a book version in 1963. Jünger himself did not choose to include it in the 1960 edition of his works, dismissing it as one of several early expressionist-influenced texts that he had mostly burned. It did finally make it into the 1978 Klett-Cotta edition of his works.[13]

Written at about the same time as *Battle as Inner Experience*, *Sturm* includes some reflections that are similar to passages in the essay, and the title figure has many characteristics that resemble those of Jünger himself. Yet there are enough differences to clearly mark Sturm as a fictional figure. In contrast to Jünger, Sturm was pursuing a doctorate in zoology before the war and was also something of a bohemian. Sturm's reflections, even if they resemble some from Jünger's essays, are clearly placed in a context within which they are to be read against the views of his comrades about the war. Moreover, the turning of attention toward both Sturm as a problematic figure and the act of writing as itself a wartime problem, results in a text that pursues a new approach to the war that diverges from Jünger's

13. Ulrich Fröschle, "Sturm," in *Ernst Jünger-Handbuch*, ed. Matthias Schöning (Stuttgart: Metzler, 2014), pp. 64–65.

earlier and later texts of the period. Hans Verboven designates Sturm as an "island" in Jünger's work that seems not to
belong, and he demonstrates that it does not affirm the power
of the state and the nationalist goals of the war in the way that
Storms of Steel does.[14] Yet, the story is also not just a pessimistic
account of war. Instead, it lays out an alternative trajectory for
the relation between violence and culture that creates the possibility for freedom in the midst of catastrophe.

The Aesthetics of Violence in *Battle as Inner Experience*

To understand the significance of *Sturm* for Jünger's work, it
will be useful to juxtapose it to *Battle as Inner Experience*, which
was published just one year before *Sturm*, but which presents an
aesthetic of violence that in fact diverges from the 1923 story.
In *Battle as Inner Experience*, Jünger places war at the center of human culture. "War is that which forms humans and
their times into what they are."[15] The violence of war becomes
the source for all the other structures of human culture, and
Jünger uses the metaphor of the sculptor or the ironsmith to
describe war as that which "hammers, chisels, and hardens"
individuals into a new form, and this forming of humans in the
experience of war has the effect of establishing a structure for
the rest of the world as well.[16] Because Jünger consistently uses
visual metaphors in order to describe this forming effect of violence on human character,[17] Thomas Nevin criticizes "Jünger's
convinced antirationalism," in which "he presents images, not

14. Hans Verboven, *Die Metapher als Ideologie: Eine kognitiv-semanti-
sche Analyse der Kriegsmetaphorik im Frühwerk Ernst Jüngers* (Heidelberg:
C. Winter, 2003), pp. 231–43.

15. Ernst Jünger, *Der Kampf als inneres Erlebnis*, in *Sämtliche Werke*,
vol. 7, *Essays I: Betrachtungen zur Zeit* (Stuttgart: Klett-Cotta, 1980), p. 11.
All translations my own.

16. Ibid.

17. Ibid.

arguments," in which "the images *are* the arguments."[18] According to this interpretation, Jünger's reliance on visuality creates an aestheticization that overruns the individual and the literary word, establishing a "language of might" and "a voluntarist notion of force" that creates a "submersion of the individual in the nexus of power."[19]

But in criticizing Jünger for subordinating the individual to power, this interpretation reduces the recipient of the aesthetic moment to a helpless and "victimized spectator,"[20] when in fact Jünger frames the spectator not as a victim but as a creator. "And if war is within us, it is also everywhere. For we form the world, nothing less, spectators in the most creative sense."[21] While Jünger's stance might be interpreted as an ideology that justifies the soldierly sacrifice, Jünger's sovereign attitude participates in a more complex process of sacrifice than the term "victimized spectator" expresses. If he emphasizes, in a reference to Heraclitus, that "war, the father of all things, is also our father," he hastens to add that "not only is war our father, but also our son. We conceived it and it conceived us. We are hammered and chiseled, but we are also those who swing the hammer and set the chisel, at once smith and spraying steel, martyrs of our own making, and driven by our own drives."[22] In this conception humans are not simply victims of violence but the actors who inflict this violence, and it is this relationship between violence and action that becomes the focus of Jünger's reflections on the relation between war and culture.

18. Thomas Nevin, *Ernst Jünger and Germany: Into the Abyss, 1914–1945* (Durham, NC: Duke Univ. Press, 1996), pp. 72–73.

19. Nevin, *Ernst Jünger and Germany*, p. 74; Russell A. Berman, *The Rise of the Modern German Novel: Crisis and Charisma* (Cambridge, MA: Harvard Univ. Press, 1986), p. 216.

20. Berman, *Rise of the Modern German Novel*, p. 225.

21. Jünger, *Kampf als inneres Erlebnis*, p. 11.

22. Ibid., p. 12.

Consequently, Jünger's aestheticization of war also does not accord well with Bohrer's interpretation of Jünger's aesthetics as an aesthetics of the sudden. Bohrer interprets the sudden moment as "the annihilation of continuity by the ecstatic moment,"[23] and sees these epiphanic moments as that which "characterizes all of modern literature."[24] Bohrer's use of the epiphanic moment in order to define modern literature (by which he means writers such as Jünger, James Joyce, and Virginia Woolf) is accurate in its characterization of modernism to the extent that all these writers were indeed searching for a kind of metaphysical experience that is grounded in art rather than a discursive rationality. This search was born of a dissatisfaction, on the one hand, with a rationality that could not achieve any kind of valid metaphysical significance and, on the other hand, with a reality that had lost a metaphysical grounding in the course of a secularization process. It is this same metaphysical dissatisfaction that Freud is perhaps describing when he indicates that life only recovers its "full content" in war. The turn to art as the place of such an ecstatic experience was a kind of last-ditch effort by writers committed both to the sacred as an essential human experience and to secularization as an irreversible reality.[25] Bohrer locates this fullness of content in the epiphanic moment of art as well as in the moment of horror in war.

But it is not clear that these epiphanic moments might exist as any kind of a cultural program that can "question every sort of anticipated continuity."[26] Bohrer distinguishes a pure aesthetic

23. Karl Heinz Bohrer, *Suddenness: On the Moment of Aesthetic Appearance*, trans. Ruth Crowley (New York: Columbia Univ. Press, 1994), p. 50.

24. Ibid., pp. 58–59.

25. Bohrer also notes that both the turn to aestheticism and the turn to war were parallel rejections of bourgeois culture, embodied in the work of Thomas Mann and Ernst Jünger, respectively. Bohrer, *Ästhetik des Schreckens*, p. 128.

26. Bohrer, *Suddenness*, p. 59.

approach in which the sudden moment is retained in its pure spectacle from an ideological approach in which this sudden moment is then fitted into a religious conception. Bohrer criticizes the political tendency to domesticate the radicality of the sudden moment, to reintegrate it into an ordered continuity with "new, parareligious contents."[27] But the character of the sudden moment is necessarily momentary, as it has no positive contents, but rather only exists as a moment of destructive violence. Thus, in privileging the moment in which "dialogue ceases, and there is only the feeling of being struck by the figure or phenomena that 'appear,'"[28] Bohrer is indeed affirming the experience of a "victimized spectator," who is struck dumb by the spectacle. His attempt to adumbrate a modernist cultural project based on suddenness as an aesthetic principle ends up reducing the aesthetic experience to a mute blinding by the appearance.

Jünger in fact describes this experience as an experience of violence, that is, a destructive sweeping away of a previous order. As such, this violence will always be immediately superseded by some type of ordering. Here, Jünger presents an interpretation of the sudden moment as a "glowing current that cools into order."[29] Bohrer's desire to hold onto this suddenness and freeze it into an aesthetic principle is a vain attempt to escape all ordering, and his attack on Jünger's "decisionistic style"[30] for reintegrating the aesthetic moment into a parareligious ideology is disingenuous to the extent that any hypostatization of the moment into an empty and emptying image of the now will always lead in the next moment into a new ordering. Jünger at least is clear about this process.

27. Ibid., pp. 60–61.
28. Ibid., p. 60.
29. Jünger, *Kampf als inneres Erlebnis*, p. 11.
30. Bohrer, *Suddenness*, p. 60.

But if Bohrer reduces the aesthetics of violence to the empty experience of the now and thereby caricatures this experience, Jünger's descriptions of violence do not in fact outline an overwhelming of the subject by the immediacy of aesthetic experience, but rather attempts by the subject to come to terms with violence and horror. Moreover, though his earliest descriptions of these aesthetic moments are connected with the horror of war, this horror does not result from the pure fear and shock of the violence and destruction, as Bohrer argues. Rather, the true experience of horror is a cultural experience, "the first harbinger of reason,"[31] in which violence is contrasted with aesthetic pleasure. Jünger presents an example of such an emphatic moment of horror in *Battle as Inner Experience*: "Once, at the beginning of an offensive, I walked through a town in which the inhabitants had escaped just with their bare lives. A comrade nudged me with a smile and pointed to a house, whose roof and walls were full of cracks. A display window had strangely preserved itself in the midst of the beginning destruction. It held a whole row of women's hats. A few days earlier, in the late evening of a battle, searching for a fallen friend, I pulled apart the bodies in a pile of corpses. Suddenly a well-fed rat leapt at me out of the uniform of one of the corpses. Nevertheless, this experience did not shake me as much as the ghostly contrast between the blasted street and the shining tinsel of painted straw, silk, and brightly colored feathers that reminded one of feminine hands and the thousand superfluities that color our life."[32] The key is not the pure visuality of the image, as with the rats.[33] Rather,

31. Ibid., p. 18.
32. Ibid., pp. 23–24.
33. Cf. Berman, who argues that Jünger's aesthetics is one in which the "visual *Gestalt* displaces the terms of writing." Russell A. Berman, "Written Right Across Their Faces: Leni Riefenstahl, Ernst Jünger, and Fascist Modernism," in *Modern Culture and Critical Theory: Art, Politics, and the Legacy of the Frankfurt School* (Madison: Univ. of Wisconsin Press, 1989), p. 103.

as Martin Meyer points out, Jünger's aesthetic is based on the contrast between violence and culture, the blasted street and the shining tinsel.[34] Such a contrast is not so much visual as conceptual—based on the viewer's ability to step back and gaze upon the scene with a detached sense of the contrast to a cultural order. The contrast here is not between images and words but between immersion in an experience and the interruption of this immersion that creates a contrast in perspective. Jünger describes another example of such horror that results not from a vision but from the contrast between hand-to-hand combat in a house and dance music coming from an orchestrion on an upper floor: "At the beginning of the war we stormed a house that used to be a restaurant. We penetrated into the barricaded cellar and wrestled in the dark with an animal-like bitterness while the house was already burning above us. Suddenly, probably occasioned by the heat of the fire, the automatic playing of an orchestrion began upstairs. I will never forget how the carefree blare of the dance music mixed in with the yelling of the fighters and the rattle of the dying."[35] There are two aspects to this horror. In the first place, it results from the experience of violence that destroys the achievements of culture. The feeling of stability and harmony projected by both the women's hats and the dance music is undermined by the violence that immediately destroys the entire cultural world. In this sense, the horrific moment functions as the sudden experience that is opposed to all continuity, but the moment can only do this to the extent that it is destroying cultural order, and the moment of suddenness is over as soon as this destruction occurs. That is, a sustained aesthetic of the sudden moment cannot exist because this aesthetic is ultimately based on the single moment of the destruction of order. This moment cannot linger or be repeated

34. Martin Meyer, *Ernst Jünger* (Munich: Carl Hanser, 1990), p. 49.
35. Jünger, *Kampf als inneres Erlebnis*, p. 24.

until a new order is established or the previously existing order is reestablished. Moreover, though the moment does involve the destruction of culture and its specific forms, the crucial role of women's hats or the orchestrion in bringing out the horror of violence indicates that the epiphanic character of the violence is not based in the purity of the moment. Rather, violence attains horror only as an opposite to human culture. Violence does not break into the human order. Instead, the human order creates the stability and continuity that define change as violence and horror. One can only experience violence from the perspective of order and not the other way around.

In spite of this dependence of violence on the prior establishment of order, Jünger understands the moment of destruction as the beginning of a process of creation. He means by this that such moments of violence demonstrate that violence and destruction underlie all cultural order and make up the brutal reality of the world that culture tries to ignore but cannot escape. By reminding a culture of this underlying truth of the world, such moments of destruction bring culture back to its foundations in violence. Consequently, the descriptions of this contrast in *Battle as Inner Experience* retain a sardonic tone in which the finery of culture is spiritually undermined by the destructive violence in the minds of the soldier-spectators. There is no affirmation of culture itself, and the narrator assumes an aesthetic stance that abstracts from the violence in order to appreciate the contrast between violence and culture as itself an aesthetic experience that can only be appreciated from the god-like perspective of a kind of Nietzschean individual. This individual aesthetic perspective is the only escape from the scenes in the text that describe a total subjugation of the individual subject to a subject-dissolving horror: "The dark curtain of horror abruptly rushes up before the mind in the last fire, yet the frozen mouth could no longer pronounce what lay in wait behind it."[36] In this description of the last horrified gaze of the dying soldier, Jünger seems to be affirming the moment of horror. However, the real horror that Jünger is here describing is the horror not of a particular scene but of death itself. It is the same unspeakable image that Freud refers to as the experience of death that no living person can share because "it is indeed impossible to imagine our own death."[37] This image of the horror of death that destroys the possibility of expression is a problem not just of war but of life itself. Nor is it the endpoint of Jünger's text, but its starting point, and the depiction of violence attempts to work its way beyond such a dissolution of subjectivity in order to affirm the meaning of violence for life.

The text here lays out two alternatives, the dissolution or the assertion of the individual subject, which become the two ways in which Jünger describes the causes of violence in war, leading to two contradictory ways of understanding how culture relates to violence. In some passages, Jünger takes a Freudian approach and describes how people become like animals without culture, caught up in an orgy of violence in which the desire to kill the enemy overcomes all cultural achievements. "In battle, which tears all agreements from man like the patched-up rags of a beggar, the animal rises up out of him like a monster from the depths of his soul."[38] Jünger provides several examples of how this animal instinct rises to the surface when soldiers encounter the enemy, especially in hand-to-hand combat, when this bloodlust "concentrates all striving around one desire: to throw oneself on the opponent, grab him, as the blood demands, without weapon, in a frenzy, with the wild grasp of the fist. It has been so from the beginning."[39] This

36. Ibid., p. 25.
37. Freud, "Thoughts for the Times on War and Death," p. 289.
38. Jünger, *Kampf als inneres Erlebnis*, pp. 15–16.
39. Ibid., pp. 12–13.

understanding of violence as an ineradicable instinct caricatures both primitive man as an animal and the moment of
battle as a disintegration of culture.

At other points in the essay, however, Jünger does not con-
centrate on underlying aggressive drives that overcome cultural
order, but rather on the way in which a culture must always
establish itself in violent competition with other cultures in
order to survive. Here, the focus is not on aggressive drives but
on the violence that is necessary for a culture to establish its
existence against competing cultures: "Though all freedom, all
greatness, and all culture were born in the idea, in a situation of
calm, they can only be preserved, spread, or lost through war.
Only through war did great religions become the heritage of
the entire earth, did the most able races shoot out of their dark
roots into the light, did uncounted slaves become free men. War
is as little a human institution as the sex drive. It is a natural law,
and we will therefore never be able to escape from its spell. We
cannot deny it, or it will devour us."[40] Here, though he again
indicates the instinctive origins of violence in his reference to
the sex drive, Jünger also indicates that violence comes about as
the result of the development of the will of a people to establish
itself through battle. Jünger affirms that culture first originates
in the calmness of the idea. But if the idea is the ultimate source
of culture, violence is not its opposite, as war is necessary for
preserving the structures of culture against competing cultures.
Rather than being an aggressive instinct, the violence of war is
more properly a kind of discipline of the will that must establish itself against instinctual behavior. "If we consider a culture
or its living carrier, the people, as a constantly growing sphere,
then the will, the unconditioned and reckless will to preserve
and expand, that is, the will to battle, is the magnetic center
through which its structure is established. If this center loses its

40. Ibid., p. 40.

force, it must fragment into atoms."[41] This discipline of the will must be at the basis of every culture for Jünger because once a culture loses this will to battle, it will disintegrate at the first challenge to its order.

Aesthetic Play and Individual Sovereignty

In this alternative understanding of the source of violence in discipline rather than instinct, Jünger establishes courage as the primary virtue in relation to violence. "Courage is the devotion of the individual person with the force of an iron commitment, the positing of the idea against the material, without regard for what might happen. Courage means to bind oneself as an individual to the cross for one's cause. Courage means, in the last shudder of the nerves and with a failing breath, to affirm the idea for which one stood and fell. To the devil with a time that seeks to rob us of courage and men!"[42] In this definition of courage as the ultimate virtue, Jünger establishes a notion of sacrifice of the material for the ideal that brings the encounter with violence back into the order and discipline of culture as embodied in the idea for which the soldier sacrifices his material life. Jünger thus lays out an alternative to the "violence as instinct" theory that Freud established as the way to understand the relation between violence and civilization as diametrical opposites. By linking the particular violence of war to a kind of discipline, Jünger places war within the ambit of culture as that which establishes and defines this discipline. Precisely because war requires discipline, it must participate in a culture that could provide its form.

However, because Jünger still retains ideas of the instinctual character of aggression and the elemental significance of violence, his move toward a linking of culture and violence is

41. Ibid., p. 41.
42. Ibid., p. 49.

incomplete. In the end, he shifts the focus of his aesthetics away from the character of a cultural order and toward the violence itself, devoid of culture. Instead of recognizing the priority of the cultural order, Jünger concentrates his attention on the act of sacrifice. For what is extraordinary about Jünger's particular notion of sacrifice is that the content of the idea for which the soldier sacrifices is not important. "It is not important *for what* we are fighting, but only *how* we fight.... The fight, the commitment of the person, even if it is for the smallest idea, weighs heavier than any deliberations over good and evil."[43] The fact of heroic sacrifice becomes itself the highest value, and the details of ideology for which one is fighting are insignificant for Jünger. As a result, Jünger, on the one hand, affirms the necessity of facing down violence to overcome it in an affirmation of an idea and, on the other hand, denies the importance of the idea, insisting that it is not the idea that is significant but only the confrontation with violence, the act of courage itself, independent of the ends to which it is put. The combination of the understanding of human violence as an instinctive and undifferentiated drive and the opposing notion that this violence is a disciplined establishment of order leads in the end to a fetishistic approach to the moment of sacrifice. What is important is not the ideal to be affirmed through the sacrifice. Rather, the encounter with violence itself is the crucial issue, and this encounter becomes the measure of value in Jünger's aesthetics of violence, regardless of the goal.

The consequence of this approach is that Jünger moves toward an affirmation of any type of aesthetic play that maintains a connection to danger and demonstrates a sovereign attitude. For example, he points out the extravagant character of soldiers who play in the face of danger: two soldiers who dressed as women with umbrellas when moving through a

43. Ibid., p. 74.

crumbling town, Scottish soldiers who begin an attack by kick-
ing a soccer ball into the opposing trenches, a lieutenant who
discovers a means of blowing up a grenade over his head without being harmed by it. His commentary on these examples
emphasizes the sovereignty of the subject that is willing to face
danger in a playful manner. "Then one felt that this collection
of sound effects, these roaring storms of steel, however greedily
they might rise up, were still only machinery, only stage curtains, that first attained meaning through the play that humans
performed before them."[44] The key for Jünger is not the violence
itself in its suddenness, nor the culture that is to be affirmed
in the individual's sacrifice, but rather the aesthetic play with
which the individual reacts to the reality of violence.

The ultimate goal of this play is not the establishment of
any cultural ideal, nor even the recognition of the reality of
violence underlying culture, but the affirmation of individual
sovereignty over violence. By shifting the focus of the sacrifice
away from the ideal being affirmed and toward the action itself
as a kind of play, Jünger develops an aesthetics of violence in
which the cultural element is subordinated to the individual
will and ethical considerations are replaced by a focus on aesthetic pleasure. This subordination of culture and community
is the result of the aestheticizing impulse that Jünger outlines
at the end of *Battle as Inner Experience*: "All goals are ephem-
eral, and only the movement is eternal; it produces unendingly
majestic and merciless dramas. Only a few are allowed to lose
themselves in their sublime purposelessness as in a work of art
or in the starry heavens. But whoever felt in this war only the
negation, only one's own suffering and not the affirmation, the
higher movement, experienced it as a slave. Such people had no
inner, but only an outer, experience."[45] Jünger denies here the

44. Ibid., pp. 60–61.
45. Ibid., p. 103.

importance of the spiritual order while affirming the movement of sacrifice as a drama that sets itself beyond both all suffering and all morality, even as it depends upon the negation of the material and the consequent ethical movement for its effect. Jünger's aesthetic is based on an affirmation of the participation in the formal structure of sacrifice without his affirmation of a specific goal of the sacrifice. He only affirms the act of sacrifice itself rather than the ideal for which the sacrifice is made, as if the ultimate meaning of human activity were the aesthetic pleasure that it provides. The movement of sacrifice consequently does not follow that of a Kantian understanding of the sublime, as Oliver Kohns argues,[46] because the point for Kant is not just the aesthetic pleasure but also the ethical content that is being affirmed by the sacrifice.[47] Jünger's particular mode of affirming courage in the face of danger results in an aesthetics of play in which the point of the play is to demonstrate a nonchalance in the face of violence, a kind of sovereignty of the subject that affirms destruction.[48] Though violence provides the backdrop for the subject's activity, living on "even when men and wars are long gone," this violence is still not the focus of Jünger's reflections. The victims of sacrifice do not come into view. Rather, Jünger's attention rests on the subject's sovereign attitude toward destruction and violence.

46. Oliver Kohns, "An Aesthetics of the Unbearable: The Cult of Masculinity and the Sublime in Ernst Jünger's 'Der Kampf als inneres Erlebnis' (Battle as an Inner Experience)," *Image [&] Narrative* 14, no. 3 (2013): 141–50; here, pp. 144–45.

47. Immanuel Kant, *Critique of Judgment*, trans. Werner S. Pluhar (Indianapolis: Hackett, 1987), p. 121.

48. Jünger, *Kampf als inneres Erlebnis*, p. 103. This structure of sacrifice as a form of sovereignty is similar to Bataille's conception. See Georges Bataille, *La Souveraineté*, in *Oeuvres Complètes* (Paris: Gallimard, 1976), vol. 8, p. 270; David Pan, *Sacrifice in the Modern World: On the Particularity and Generality of Nazi Myth* (Evanston, IL: Northwestern Univ. Press, 2012), pp. 82–92.

But by interpreting sacrifice exclusively as part of the sovereignty of the individual over violence, Jünger also ends up establishing the priority of the individual over the community. This focus on the individual at the expense of a community becomes evident in the isolation of the narrator in *Battle as Inner Experience*. There are no descriptions of relationships to others in this essay, only passing encounters, and it seems as if every figure is a solitary one, without the possibility of developing more extended human relationships. We see this most clearly in the section entitled "Contrast," in which Jünger has a romantic encounter with a young woman whom he designates at first as a prostitute and then describes in more detail as the wife of a French soldier on the other side of the front. The narrator describes the encounter cursorily, indicating the loneliness of both the narrator and the woman: "Everyone is very alone in this great landscape, over which the breath of war blows."[49] Afterward, "when we separate at the doorway, she says, 'Je ne t'oublierai pas.' I will not forget you. It sounds genuine. I walk over the bridge back into town, hands in my coat pockets, head bowed. The spurs sound with every step."[50] In spite of the affirmation of the woman, there is no indication that the narrator is much affected by the encounter, who in the next sentence joins a comrade to go to a café before returning to the front, and the episode is never mentioned again. It seems to be an example of the erotic release that the narrator describes as an accompaniment to the war experience, another sort of intoxication that replaces the frenzy of war but does not present an opposite to it. "Two impulses confront us in this way as the causes of this flood of sensuous phenomena: The urge to life, to express oneself again in a heightened way, and the flight into the thicket of intoxication, in order to forget in the

49. Jünger, *Kampf als inneres Erlebnis*, p. 68.
50. Ibid., p. 69.

lust the threatening dangers."[51] Both the urge to life and the intoxication as escape become isolated individual experiences that do not establish any human relationships, but only stave off an underlying fear and isolation. There is one moment in the essay in which the narrator lapses into a sentimental evocation of a budding young love between a German student soldier and a French farm girl, in which "two lips grazed the man's ear," but the interlude quickly concludes with the death of the soldier shortly thereafter: "He stood clearly in the hail of bullets, the whiff of the kisses still in his hair. Death approached as a friend, a ripe stalk fell with a slash."[52] The description of a more enduring human relationship serves in this episode to merely underlie the futility of such relations in the context of war, and the reader is thrown back on the recourse to a self-centered sovereignty in the isolated individual.

War and Culture in *Sturm*

Coming from a reading of *Battle as Inner Experience*, it would be easy to read *Sturm* as more of the same, especially as *Sturm* includes very similar depictions of horror at the front, and in fact Bohrer's reading of the story is similar to his reading of the essay, emphasizing the decadence of the literary language, the focus on "sensationalist perceptions," and the "escalation of an introverted subjectivism."[53] Yet, a look at the structure of the story reveals a very different depiction of the war experience, even as very similar images make up the material of the text. One of the key differences that Bohrer has described is the way in which *Sturm* is as much about writing and art as about war. Not only is the title character a writer and one of his

51. Ibid., p. 37.
52. Ibid., pp. 39–40.
53. Bohrer, *Die Ästhetik des Schreckens*, pp. 134, 136.

three comrades a painter, the text makes constant explicit and implicit references to works of art, books, and literary styles.[54]

As in the orchestrion scene in *Battle as Inner Experience*, the contrast between violence and culture is the key to aesthetic effect in *Sturm*. In describing the construction of the trench-works, Sturm reflects that the focus on war allowed the spiritual to become all the more meaningful: "Precisely because of the sharp contrast that it afforded, however, the few hours that one could dedicate here to spiritual pursuits allowed one to reach the pinnacle of pleasure." The refinement of spiritual pursuits is sharpened by the contrast with war, yet he indicates in the very next lines that it may be war itself that is the source of the most enduring and striking aesthetic effects:

> Perhaps it was the clarity and certainty of these battle struc-tures that gripped him so. He remembered how, on a street near the harbor of the northern German city where he was raised, he had often closely observed an ancient city tower, in whose windowless, powerful, foursquare structure only nar-row arrow slits were cut.
>
> This tower loomed as a threatening gesture over a mass of gables. From the frozen sea of competing architectural styles it alone rose forth as a closed and solid unity. Only war brought forth such manifestations. When at night Sturm strode among the gun emplacements on the traverse and saw behind each a well-armed figure on solitary watch, he had the same feeling every time: gigantic and fabulous.

In contrast to the sea of shifting styles in art, the functional architecture of war creates a kind of clarity and unity that seems to be the source of a more fundamental experience for Sturm.

Yet, even if Sturm sees battle here as the motivating basis of this aesthetic experience, there is also an essential transformative

54. Ibid., p. 130.

effect that culture and works of art contribute to this experience. In describing the reproduction of Hobbema's *Allee* that he has hung on the wall of his trench shelter, he remarks: "When in the evening a last beam of sunlight streamed through the shaft, blue-gray tobacco smoke swirling through it, a quiet golden glow emanated from this masterpiece that reached the furthest corner of the desolate cellar." The work of art does not simply provide a contrast to the war; it actually penetrates and permeates its surroundings in order to transform them in its image. The exigencies of battle and the refinements of culture interact with each other in order to create the significant aesthetic experience. As opposed to the scenes of contrast in *Battle as Inner Experience*, culture is not undermined or satirized by the relation to a violence that is constantly destroying it. Rather, in a reversal, the war begins to take on structures from works of art.

Sturm continues on to describe a similar dialectical relationship between human activity and the war as a kind of independent force in itself. After describing the way in which the war had transformed the agricultural landscape into a new terrain with new creatures, he emphasizes that the changes were in the end the result of human activity. "Man had done all of that. In his soul a change occurred, and the landscape received a new face. Man was at the root of everything, yet this effect was so monumental that he sometimes failed to recognize his part in it. These nights in the wasteland, illuminated by flashes of lightning and dazzled by the uncertain shimmer of flares, gave a true reflection of his soul." Even though human activity has transformed the landscape, the power of this transformation is so violent that humans no longer recognize it as their own work and see it as if it were like a force of nature. Yet, the changes in the landscape are in fact a result of changes in the human soul. The alienation from the landscape of trench war results then from an alienation of humans from their own activity.

This alienation is not a specific consequence of war but of a broader phenomenon that encompasses both the war front and the cultural situation in general. Sturm recognizes that he has "become a different man" through the experience of the war, but that this change in himself was something that was preparing itself before the war began. "What had thrust him into the army, in the midst of work on his doctorate? It was the war, which he had carried in his blood like any other real son of his time, long before, a fiery beast, he entered the actual arena. For the intellect had become too refined; it sprang like a tightrope walker back and forth between unbridgeable contradictions. How much longer before it disappeared into an abyss of insane laughter?" Sturm's existence before the war was already alienated, and his intellectual pursuits had become a kind of exaggerated and unstable tightrope walk that was about to lead to a collapse in the dance between intellectual oppositions. This metaphor links Sturm's pre-war existence to the frantic dance between life and death that characterizes the front soldier and led to the suicide of the soldier in the latrine, described at the beginning of the story: "He could well understand that someone who found himself dancing between life and death would suddenly awaken like a sleepwalker between abysses and let himself fall." Though the fall into suicide seems incomparable to Sturm's fall into laughter, both are in fact instances of a failure of self-representation that undermines the self-worth of the individual in the dance over the abyss. In both the pre-war and the wartime alienation, the key experience seems to be one of being forced to jump between opposites and to be in perpetual motion without having any individual power or freedom to affect one's destiny. This activity without freedom then becomes the key problem of the story, and the narrative movement between descriptions of the front and the embedded stories of life at home revolve around this problem of alienation, attempting to imagine and establish a basis for freedom.

The difficulty is that Sturm's invocation of the war itself as that which breaks the cycle of alienation leads into a contradictory description of the war as both alienating and emancipatory. "The mysterious pendulum that resides in everything alive, that ineffable world-reason, had suddenly swung to the other side and sought with the might of a fist, with the force of a tremendous explosion, to force a breach through the brittle masonry and open the way to new paths." While the war is part of a "world-reason" that seems to work independently of individual human will, its effect is in the end to destroy the paralyzing constraints on human activity and action of the pre-war era. The war, then, remains both a part of a process of alienation and the singular event that breaks through such alienation in order to render human activity once again free. This contradictory aspect of the war leads Jünger to two alternative readings of the war experience that he works out on the one hand in *Battle as Inner Experience* and on the other hand in *Sturm*, the latter work standing out and apart from the rest of Jünger's work of the 1920s in its unique solution to the problem of alienation.

Individual and Community

The detached attitude of the narrator in *Battle as Inner Experience* returns in *Sturm* within the figure of Sturm, but the fictional account allows the reader both to contrast this particular attitude with that of others in the trenches and to thereby study this attitude itself. If writing creates meaning, war destroys it, not just directly through physical violence but indirectly by turning communities into isolated individuals. Jünger's *Sturm* describes this process in the first section of the story through the opposition between human interaction and fearful solitude. The story opens with the description of the contrast between community and individual isolation, between the late afternoon, on the one hand, in which the "[t]he platoon leaders of the third company were in the habit of spending the hours before sunset together" and in which "minor matters regained significance and were exchanged in endless conversations," and the morning hours after a night of conflict, on the other hand, during which "they walked past one another sullenly." By engaging in their afternoon talks, the group of three commanders that make up the small group around which the story revolves already sets up an example of human community that contrasts with the isolating influence of life in the trenches. Even though they are soldiers, the valuation of "minor matters" in their conversations is a key part of their war experience and in fact enables their ability to experience their time together "like sessions of the stock exchange, during which everything of importance there was evaluated." The establishment of values and the evaluation of experience takes place in these hours of conversation. For this reason, the narrator describes the soldiers as the same men as they were in peace. They "had left nothing behind that had motivated them in peacetime. They were ancients in another country and in another form of being." Their existence in the trenches was not fundamentally different than their existence at home, though the particular contradictions of regular life had become clearer. The narrator describes this contradiction as the one between the feeling of community that sometimes links the soldiers together so that they "were like brothers," on the one hand, and the loneliness during a bombardment, when each "stood alone in the darkness, howling and crashing surrounding him, blinded by sudden flashes, with nothing in his breast but endless desolation," on the other hand.

The story presents the main image of this loneliness in the soldier who has shot himself dead on the latrine, leading the other soldiers to feel most acutely "the aura of futility that shrouded a corpse." This feeling of futility is not simply a result of the violence of war, but of the impersonal character of this violence. "War played out on a gigantic scale, before which the fate of the individual disappeared." The circumstances of the First World War created an alienation of the soldiers from the battle. The battlefields were wide and empty, the fighting happened at night, and one's fate did not seem to depend on individual action but on the impersonal consequences of machine gun and artillery fire. This alienation of the soldier is the greatest danger for Sturm, who describes individuals who are overcome by it as marked for death. "You could always recognize the ones to whom these ghosts had appeared. They turned pale and haggard, and when they drew guard duty, their gaze was fixed and unmoving, pointing like their weapon over no-man's-land."

Yet, this alienation of the front soldier is not just a consequence of a mechanized and factory-produced war. Rather, the narrator describes the war as simply another example of the general alienation of modern life. "It was at base the same feeling of meaninglessness that was sometimes evoked in a melancholy mind by the barren housing blocks of factory towns—that feeling with which mass oppressed the soul." Meaninglessness is not a consequence of violence but of individual alienation, and the escape from it is not to flee from the war into peace but to avoid loneliness by creating a human connection to others, whether in the war or at home. "And just as there one hurriedly strode to the city center in order to disperse gloomy thoughts among cafés, mirrors, and lights, so one sought here to escape oneself in conversations, in drink, and in peculiar detours of the brain." The parallel between the cafés of the city and the conversations in the trenches sets up the analogy between the depiction of the war in the framing narrative and the stories of city life that Sturm tells the others during the breaks in the fighting. If Sturm recognizes that he cannot depict the war directly because he is too close to it, the detour through city life in fact recapitulates the problem of war alienation as a more general problem of modern life.

The story unfolds then as an attempt to sort out the relationship between individual alienation and a community built on words and conversation, both in war and in peace. The problem of words and writing is not just one that needs to be confronted as a problem of war writing, how to describe the indescribable in war, but as a general problem of human society, how to move from individual to community. This problem is one that the soldier on the front faces in the alienating character of the World War I battlefield, in which the opponent is rarely seen and even comrades must recede into the background during a bombardment. But Sturm also describes this situation of the World War I soldier as a consequence of a larger transformation of society that has transformed war along with it: "meaning has gradually moved over to the state, which has been ever more ruthlessly confining the functions of the individual to a specialized sphere. Today and for a long time past, one is no longer valued at what one is truly worth in and of oneself, but rather only at what one is worth in relation to the state." Sturm criticizes here the new role of the state, in which the individual only gains meaning through the relationship to the state.

If such a description of the priority of the state over the individual is expressed here as a critique, it will become for Jünger by the early 1930s a condition to be accepted and celebrated in the essays *Total Mobilization*, *The Worker*, and *On Pain*, in which he adumbrates a new conception of subjectivity that subordinates individual development to the needs of the state and its technological apparatus both in war and in a kind of peace that still develops the industrial capacity for war. In this conception, war is not just an affair of the soldier, but it involves the collective effort of an entire nation in order to develop the industrial capacity that is crucial for winning the kind of war of materiel and of attrition that characterized World War I. In these essays, Jünger reconsiders the alienation of the soldier and the worker as cogs within industrial society in order to reinterpret them as the figures of a new age and as the means by which a nation can gain a kind of overall freedom in spite of the subordination of the individuals within it. He indicates that the work within industrial society that the worker carries out is a new form of freedom.[55] The worker finds this freedom not in the relation to others but in the relation to the overarching *Gestalt* that is the eternal form of the nation-state. The individual relation to the *Gestalt* means that Jünger emphasizes in the worker the individual nature of experience as a confrontation with mortality and a willingness to sacrifice one's own mortality for the *Gestalt*. This individualist mode of sacrifice contrasts, however, with the kind of community that becomes the focus of *Sturm*.

Sturm's own consideration of the industrialization of war serves to underline the alienation of the front soldier from the officer corps. "Before the war there had been so much written about the intellectual improvement of the officer corps that the basic human element had been forgotten—and that was the key thing in this occupation." By contrast, Sturm himself makes the effort to converse with the soldier Kettler, in order to "open a window into the soul of the masses, in the midst of whom circumstances forced him to live." Similarly, the focus of the entire story is on the group of three officers, who make up a small community with each other during the pauses in the war

55. Ernst Jünger, *Der Arbeiter: Herrschaft und Gestalt* (Hamburg: Hanseatische Verlagsanstalt, 1932), p. 65.

that allow them some time to converse. The building of community in the trenches becomes the antidote to the alienation of the individual who has become meaningless as a functionalized member of the state. The community becomes a new living thing that "develops according to the laws of organic nature," and as Sturm writes: "Just as marriage makes a couple more similar with time, so does every long-lived community alter its members fundamentally." The story describes how the three characters of the story transform each other in such a way that they are able to overcome the alienation of a mechanized society in a manner that is similar to the process of a marriage. As opposed to both the meaningless "American flirtation" described by Freud and the short erotic interludes of *Battle as Inner Experience*, *Sturm* attempts to lay out the way in which human relationships effect long-lasting change in the personalities of the individuals, bringing these individuals out of their isolation into a collective development. Like in a marriage, "[t]he remarkable thing is that this process actually brings about an alteration of the personality." The individuals are transformed into personalities through their mutual interaction. They are able to develop as individuals to the extent that they all participate in the development of their community, and they thereby turn the violence of war into something that has become meaningful. This meaning does not lie in the affirmation of individual courage and sovereignty, but in their participation in the group, and this participation in the group becomes the basis for culture in a war context.

In order to investigate this possibility of a war culture, the story provides different examples of cultural representation, and each member of the group of officers has his own relationship to culture. Döhring uses culture as a style that can impress others, and in his speech "[i]t gave him pleasure to adopt a foreign style that he soon let drop again." Hugersdorf was a painter before the war who describes himself on the one hand as a "pure colorist" and on the other hand as a painter who is fundamentally interested in "ecstasy." This expressionist conception of art leads him into a bitter argument with Döhring because of the latter's focus on style over substance, but the story will go on to undermine the positions of both the pure stylist and the ecstatic artist.

The narrator characterizes Sturm as someone who can distance himself from his experience. As a writer, Sturm is particular in that "he could abstract from the events of the day to an unusual degree," and his stories help his comrades achieve an "escape from the present." This escape can be an advantage to the extent that it allows the comrades to better face their war situation and can in fact be the source of new community and creation, but it can be a disadvantage in that the stories seem also to be superfluous and alienated from their reality of violence. As Volker Mergenthaler and Peter Uwe Hohendahl point out,[56] this conflict between a violent reality and the constructions of culture, between war and writing, becomes a key one for the story. But whereas *Battle as Inner Experience* and *Total Mobilization* tend to denigrate the superfluities of culture in comparison with the deeper reality of violence, the use of a fictional genre in *Sturm* seems to create an inherent valorization of culture and writing. If Sturm exemplifies the kind of distanced stance that Jünger takes in his essays, in *Sturm* the distance does not become a way for the individual to transcend violence through a sovereign attitude. Instead, the distance allows Sturm to reflect on the war experience through writing, creating a kind of antidote to the alienating aspects of war.

56. Volker Mergenthaler, *"Versuch, ein Dekameron des Unterstandes zu schreiben": Zum Problem narrative Kriegsbegegnung in den frühen Prosatexten Ernst Jüngers* (Heidelberg: C. Winter, 2001), pp. 109–13; Peter Uwe Hohendahl, "Krieg und Romankrise: Ernst Jüngers Erzählung 'Sturm,'" *Zeitschrift für deutsche Philologie* 133, no. 2 (2014): 247–66; here, pp. 254–58.

The link to marriage becomes the main means for trans-forming the war experience, since much of *Sturm* consists of stories within the story in which Sturm tells the stories of love that he has been writing in his free time. Sturm's first story is a short vignette that uses an ornamental style in order to intro-duce the figure of Tronck, "a thirty-year-old who saw his calling in an elegant appearance." As Sturm explains, his intention with this figure is "to explore the tension between the drive for action in a singular man and the constraint placed on this drive by the frame in which his environment fixes him." Sturm uses this conflict between the individual will and the framing effect of circumstances in order to investigate the form of freedom of the front soldier. "We have subordinated ourselves to the prog-ress of a great, necessary event; our own will—that which we call freedom or personality—often stands in contradiction to it. And that which we try to accomplish on this miserable piece of ground—the free unfolding of the personality in the midst of the most stringent constraints that one can imagine—is what I'd like to bring to full expression in the person of Tronck." In order to describe the effort of the soldier to maintain freedom in a situation of constraint, Sturm chooses the decisions about dress and manner of a city dandy because it is precisely the vio-lence and threat of death that bring out the appreciation for the ornamental and aesthetic. "It is precisely then, when life is threatened, that it strives to connect with as much as possible; it sends out light and radio signals like a sinking ship." While this aesthetic heightening seems similar to the scenes of individual bravado in *Battle as Inner Experience*, the soldiers with umbrel-las or blowing grenades over their heads, there is a difference between the willful staging of the violent moment in order to delight in the individual's sovereignty over death and the con-flict between individual freedom and external constraint that is the focus with Tronck and Sturm. In the former case, the issue is the individual's contempt for constraints, while in the latter the issue is the attempt to recognize constraints while also pursuing individual goals.

Sturm's second story displays a similar dialectical conflict, this time in a way that is more directly related to war and written in an Expressionist style. The main figure here, Ensign Kiel, is a soldier who is currently away from the war in a city but still retains the kind of instinctual aggression and restless habits in the night that he knows from the front. In transferring these habits into the city, he is overcome by a sexual lust that drives him into the night to seek a woman, finally settling on a prostitute. The key moment of this story arrives as he awakens next to the prostitute, considers her "mask-like" face, and recalls a moment of budding love before the war: "Suddenly, out of some dark sensation of contrast, emerged the image of a half-forgotten figure: a girl whom he had loved with an intensity inconceivable to him now, although in boyish bashfulness he had never exchanged a word with her." Though the war situation brings out a "regression to barbarism" and "medieval passions," there are also times when "the longing for tender, lyrical sensation emerged as a fata morgana from the wreckage of a shattered culture." The war's lifting of cultural constraints and demand for the regression to primal passions does not lead to a total barbarization but in fact creates an opposing yearning for the delicate fabric of culture in human relationships. In contrast to the scene between the student and the farm girl in *Battle as Inner Experience*, this story's evocation of the refinements of culture does not have any hint of an ironic tone that would undermine the legitimacy of culture. In fact, the evocation of Kiel's yearning breaks through the heavy Expressionist style in order to present a moment of pre-war society as a genuinely utopian moment.

The structure of *Sturm* repeats this mutually reinforcing relationship between the brutality of war and the refinement of culture in the structure of events in which Sturm's stories are interrupted by the fall of shells and the start of enemy attacks. The stories function as short oases of culture in between the brutal scenes of war. Even more, they are able to reestablish the threads of social relationships that are constantly being threatened by the random death and alienating violence of the bombardments. As Sturm points out during a bombardment, the way to regain his sense of self is to achieve the ability to represent himself to himself: "He tried to imagine how he looked: a trembling bundle in a torn uniform, with a blackened, sweat-streaked face and staring eyes in which fear could be read." He can only describe this condition of alienated and individualized horror from an outside perspective, through the effort of becoming an observer of his own condition. Yet, this effort in fact accomplishes the escape from the condition of horror, a condition that is itself incapable of producing direct expression. The primary danger of the bombardments is to turn each soldier into an isolated and speechless individual who is totally possessed by fear. Thus, in the next sentence he tries to use words to take back possession of himself. "He stood and tried to calm his nerves through a series of curses. He thought he had talked himself back into heroism, when a new and even more terrible impact hurled him back into his hole." To reduce the experience of the front soldier to the moment of horror would be to overlook one of the primary tasks of this soldier: the constant effort to maintain a sense of self amidst the horror through a self-representational process. The challenge for the troops is to avoid becoming isolated. By representing themselves, they retain a consciousness of their adherence to a group. The possibility of speech and of representation preserves their integrity as individuals, but the ultimate goal of this whole process is to reform the group. "The individual was a weakling in times of danger. It was difficult, on the other hand, to be a coward when one was observed." The problem of representation is consequently not just an issue of transmitting the experience of war to those at home. The very ability to fight and engage in war requires the development of a context for representation. The isolated individual becomes paralyzed by fear and cannot engage in battle. It is only when the individual has the sense of performing for an audience that courage and initiative can return. Maintaining this representational quality of fighting becomes the crucial task of the World War I soldier.

The challenge for *Sturm* is not just to represent the war in a story for those at home, but to maintain war as a representation for the soldiers themselves. While this maintenance of a group cohesion and identity can only be done in battle to the extent that the soldiers are constantly aware of each other rather than being self-centered in fear, the gatherings of the officers to hear Sturm's stories during the breaks in the fighting are also indispensable for developing the web of relationships, the public sphere, so to speak, that offers the basis for the sense of community in the midst of the fighting. Here, the stories of von Horn about the tunnel fighting that he engaged in previously, self-aggrandizing as they are, have an equally important meaning for the soldiers in cementing their sense of community and cohesion. It is only to the extent that their fighting becomes a spectacle that can be beheld and then represented that it retains meaning, and this meaning is what prevents the soldiers from either committing suicide or losing their will to fight, becoming like one of the walking dead that Sturm describes early on.

The final story that Sturm tells also concerns a type of alienation that comes of a failure to represent. Falk, a figure who recalls Rönne from Gottfried Benn's *Rönne* novellas, lives within a kind of shock state, withdrawn from human society and, though he considers himself a writer, is unable to produce any writing. This inward turn is combined with a will to regression: "Sometimes he wished to be a simple animal, a plant, or some kind of life, not differentiated in the least. He hated the idea of an evolution whose ever more finely organized creatures also had to experience every torture endlessly augmented." While this desire recalls the wish to become a "clump of slime in a warm moor" in Benn's "Gesänge,"[57] Falk does not in fact succumb directly to this regressive desire. Instead, he channels this will to regression into a desire for connection, motivating his search for women. "What drove him to women was not pleasure, but a wound that burned deep down." But because he has a "dogged fury to lose oneself in the multiplicity of things," his turn to women is one that seeks intoxication in sexual experiences on the one hand and in raucous beer hall evenings on the other. This episode could easily end like the description of *eros* in *Battle as Inner Experience*, in which the soldiers fulfill in their eroticism a desire for a self-dissolving intoxication.[58]

But the story takes a new turn by recounting how Falk meets a woman in the streetcar who happens to be reading the same book as he is, Hippolyte Taine's *Balzac*. In the ensuing evening of drinks and conversation, Falk realizes that he has found a kindred spirit: "he saw comprehension. Already with the first exchange of sounds he felt it surge back to him, stimulating, electric, unanticipated. He felt himself channeled into a strange current, diverted into a fluid and mobile element whose existence had been completely hidden to him beforehand." This human connection leads him to recount his experiences on

57. Meyer points out the reference to Benn and also refers to Jünger's later statement about his fascination with this poem in his youth. Meyer, *Ernst Jünger*, pp. 44, 69; Ernst Jünger, *Annäherungen* (1970), in *Sämtliche Werke* (Stuttgart: Klett-Cotta, 1978), vol. 11, p. 372. See also Hohendahl, "Krieg und Romankrise," p. 263.

58. Jünger, *Kampf als inneres Erlebnis*, p. 36.

the front. He describes how he was moved by bloodlust during a battle into a frenzy of physical violence that cut through all nationalist and heroic war ideals. This battle frenzy takes over his consciousness. "A torrential wave gripped me and propelled me with irresistible force. I raced like a screaming devil over the ground and pitched headfirst into the carnage. My rifle was loaded, but I carried it like a club and struck out around me, without distinguishing between friend and foe, until I fell to the ground exhausted from loss of blood." This experience is an example of the type of war intoxication that Freud criticizes, but it is in fact precisely in its intoxication detrimental to the war effort. Not only does the basic distinction between friend and enemy dissolve, but the frenzy ends in the collapse of the soldier. The experience of war intoxication is in fact another example of the alienation of the soldier.

This self-alienation in the intoxication of war then becomes the key problem for Falk, the root of his current alienation, leading to the situation in which he "noticed how little people are essentially at home with themselves." Yet, Falk's experience does not end with this alienation. He recognizes that, in the soldiers' reaction to the war intoxication, "it was not their experience of the thing, but what they thought of it afterward, that was essential." The moment of intoxication, like the moment of horror, is not the endpoint, but the beginning of a challenge to represent the experience in a way that can reestablish both individual and communal identity. Like the other figures of Sturm's stories, Falk is caught within an alienation from others that is linked to the war experience but that reproduces itself in relationships with women. Though it is only a beginning, his encounter with the kindred spirit seems to provide a way out of his isolation through the development of a human relationship built upon a cultural community, here represented by the common interest in Balzac.

Conclusion

Writing and representation are indeed the main focus of *Sturm*, not as opposites to the war experience, but as part of its very fabric. Not only is self-representation essential in order that each soldier can act as if being watched and therefore part of a community with a history. The stories of love in *Sturm* show that the gradual development of human relationships is the key to avoiding the alienation from reality that threatens the front soldier with suicide, resignation to death, and battle frenzy. This final point is Jünger's corrective to the Freudian depiction of war as a kind of instinctual release rather than itself an outgrowth of the discipline of culture. *Sturm*'s depiction of war does not stop at the horror. Nor does it overcome the horror through an assertion of individual sovereignty, as in *Battle as Inner Experience*. Instead, the specter of alienation becomes the impetus for creating forms of communal, cultural experience that replace the alienation with a kind of freedom that expresses itself through mutual interaction with long-term consequences—participation in a communal development mediated through representations.

Seen in this way, the end of the story need not be read, as Hans-Harald Müller does,[59] as a failure to link the active and contemplative sides of Sturm's personality and a demonstration of the impossibility of writing about war. Rather, the final attack, in which Sturm burns his manuscript in order to have light in order to escape from the trench and then dies with his comrades after their refusal to surrender to an overwhelming British force, demonstrates the successful merging of action with representation. The manuscript has already served its purpose in turning the isolated individuals into a mutually

---

59. Hans-Harald Müller, *Der Krieg und die Schriftsteller: Der Kriegsroman der Weimarer Republik* (Stuttgart: J. B. Metzler, 1986), pp. 265–73.

supporting group. Moreover, the final lines of the story, in which Sturm's death is depicted as a "sinking into the eddy of an ancient melody," allows Sturm and his comrades to participate in an aestheticization of war that is not in the form of a spectacle of horror or of a subjugation to an impersonal machinery. Instead, they continue to participate in an evolving aesthetic development that links these soldiers' deaths to other similar heroic deaths.[60] The very depiction of their deaths dignifies them in the same way that Jünger would later do in *The Forest Passage* for those "forest rebels," the Norwegian Petter Moen and the German Helmuth James Graf von Moltke, both of whom died in the scattered resistance against Nazism. While *Sturm* has not yet developed a sense of the kind of justice that justifies the resistance in *The Forest Passage*, the early story does provide a vision of the kind of freedom that is at stake and is linked to the process of representation.

The importance of representation for *Sturm* makes it all the more curious that Jünger allowed his story to itself slip into publishing oblivion. Verboven suggests that the story no longer fit within his political trajectory due to its critiques of the ideological reasons for the war.[61] The contrast with *Battle as Inner Experience* shows that the story, though grounded in the earlier texts, was certainly a new departure. In the development of his work in the 1920s toward an affirmation of the functionalization of the individual into the worker type, he refuses to continue the development that *Sturm* begins and instead embraces the functionalization by the state and its need for total mobilization. The development of the community that counters this trend is obvious in the story as a key element of the front experience. Yet, Jünger seems to want to edit this

60. Hohendahl also points out this "performative" means of affirming aesthetic production in the story. Hohendahl, "Krieg und Romankrise," p. 264.

61. Verboven, *Die Metapher als Ideologie*, p. 242.

experience out of his own writerly development. That Jünger did not continue in the direction of *Sturm* in the 1920s is certainly one of the tragedies of his career. The impulse was not lost, however, and the notion of freedom that the story depicts ultimately returns in *The Forest Passage* as a source of resistance to totalitarian power, in which Jünger can unabashedly affirm: "Whatever the situation, whoever the other, the individual can become this fellow human being—and thereby reveal his native nobility."[62]

---

62. Jünger, *The Forest Passage*, p. 83.

Sturm

The platoon leaders of the third company were in the habit of spending the hours before sunset together. At this hour their nerves were rested; minor matters regained significance and were exchanged in endless conversations. If they met instead in the mornings after nights full of rain, shell-fire, and a thousand different disturbances, their thoughts were disjointed and sharp; they walked past one another sullenly or drove bad moods to outbursts that in peacetime would have resulted in weeks-long disciplinary hearings.

After a four-hour sleep, on the other hand, they awoke new men. They washed in their helmets, brushed their teeth, and lit their first cigarettes. They read the news brought by the orderlies and took their mess tins from the hay-filled warming crates. Then they strapped on their pistols and left the dugouts in order to stroll along the trenches. That was the hour at which they used to meet with Lieutenant Sturm, leader of the central platoon.

These meetings were like sessions of the stock exchange, during which everything of importance there was evaluated. The company was like an animal dug into the sand, vibrating with muscle tension while seemingly at rest. The advance had required all of their energies; now, on the defensive, the men drew together again and engaged in every kind of interaction. They were connected to the rest of mankind only by thin, fragile threads; they were isolated like wintery villages in an Alpen valley. For this reason, the individual gained in interest; the psychological drive toward knowledge that lived in every man had to satisfy itself continually with the same phenomena and grew stronger for it.

These men, whose lives together were dismissed in the imagination of those at home with a few words like "camaraderie" and "brothers in arms," had left nothing behind that had motivated them in peacetime. They were ancients in another country and in another form of being. And as such they had also brought with them the peculiar sensitivity that could grasp another person's face, his smile, or even the sound of his voice at night, and draw from it an equation between I and You.

Professors and glass-blowers, who drew watch duty together; vagrants, electricians, and university students, united on patrol; barbers and country boys, who sat next to each other in the tunnels; porters, sappers, mess orderlies, officers, and NCOs, who whispered together in the dark corners of the trenches—they all comprised a great family, in which things went not better and not worse than in any other family. There were young, always cheerful boys there, whom one couldn't pass without smiling or calling out a friendly word; fatherly types, with full beards and clear eyes, who spread a zone of respect around themselves and knew how to settle any situation with the right word; capable men of the people, quietly competent and ready with a helping hand; nonstop talkers, who withdrew during working hours to abandoned stretches of the trenches and tunnels in order to smoke or snore, but who accomplished unbelievable feats at mealtime and always talked the biggest, with astonishing good humor, during times of rest. Many men were completely overlooked; they were like commas that you read past and were often first noticed when a shot shattered their existence. Others, real stepchildren, had unpleasant faces and sat in corners alone; nothing they took on went right, and no one wanted to draw sentry duty with them. They were saddled with nicknames, and when their groups were assigned a particularly onerous special duty, like hauling munitions or running wire, it went without saying that the corporal sought them out for it. Still others knew how to coax soulful notes out of an ocarina, sing a few verses of an evening, or work driving bands, shell fragments, or hunks of chalk into delicate objects; they were for these reasons welcome companions. Between the ranks stood the walls of a northern German discipline. Beyond them contrasts were sharper and feelings more vivid, yet they broke through only in rare moments.

The strangely fleeting and sad aspects of human interaction showed themselves particularly clearly in this warring community, this life-and-death company. Like a mass of flies, they danced amongst one another but were as suddenly dispersed by a passing wind. Of course, when the mess orderlies unexpectedly brought forward grog from the kitchen or when a mild evening softened the general mood, then all the men were like brothers and drew even the rejects into their circle. When a man fell, the others stood together over his corpse; their gazes met, dark and deep. But when death stood over the trenches like a storm cloud, then it was every man for himself: he stood alone in the darkness, howling and crashing surrounding him, blinded by sudden flashes, with nothing in his breast but endless desolation.

And when, at midday, they squatted on the burnt-brown clay banks of the sentry posts, and bright butterflies fluttered over the trenches from the wasted land's blooming thistle—when the noise of battle was silent for a few short hours, and feeble jokes were accompanied by half-muffled laughter—then, often, a ghost bathed in glowing light would glide from the tunnels, stare one man or another point-blank in the face, and ask: "But why are you laughing? Why are you cleaning your weapon? Why are you groveling in the dirt here, like a worm in a corpse? Tomorrow, perhaps, everything will be forgotten like a dream in the night." You could always recognize the ones to whom these ghosts had appeared. They turned pale and haggard, and when they drew guard duty, their gaze was fixed and unmoving, pointing like their weapon over no-man's-land. When they fell, a friend would pronounce the ancient warrior's saying over their grave: "Almost as if he'd seen it coming. He was so changed recently."

Some men also suddenly disappeared; weapon, canteen, and helmet lay in a corner, left behind like the cocoon of a butterfly. After a few days or weeks they would be brought back; the military police had seized them in a train station or a tavern. Then came the court martial and transfer to another regiment.

One morning the comrades found one of these quiet men dead on the latrine, swimming in blood. His right foot was bare; it seemed that he had pointed his weapon at his heart and pulled the trigger with his toes. It was precisely one day before the relief. A shivering group stood in the mist around the prostrate corpse, which lay like a sack in the slimy, paper-flecked mud. In the countless holes made by hob-nailed boots lay a brownish black tar covered with bubbling droplets of blood, like a ruby-colored oil. Whether it was the unusual manner of death in this landscape, to which dying belonged like a flash of blinding light belonged to a shell, or the miserable spot: that day every man felt especially acutely the aura of futility that shrouded a corpse.

Someone finally tossed out a remark, as one might throw a piece of cork in the water in order to test the current: "This one shot himself dead because he was afraid of dying. And others have shot themselves because they weren't taken on as volunteers. I don't understand it." Sturm, who stood nearby, thought about the ghost. He could well understand that someone who found himself dancing between life and death would suddenly awaken like a sleepwalker between abysses and let himself fall. If honor and fatherland did not guide him on his path like fixed stars—if his body had not been toughened by the lust for battle as with a shirt of mail—he was nothing more than a mollusk, a twitching nerve ending, in the hail of fire and steel.

Of course—he thought—anyone who slacked off like that could go to the devil. One's strength was tested to the utmost here; Sturm was too much a child of his time to feel sympathy in such cases. But suddenly a quite different image switched on in his brain: an enemy attack after furious artillery fire.

There, the strongest and best had sprung out from cover, and this elite had been obliterated in the last thrust of steel, while beneath them in the tunnels the weaklings trembled and made a virtue of the saying: "Better five minutes a coward than a whole lifetime dead." Did the best and bravest receive their due here?

Yes, those who understood such things uncovered threads here that led to strange thoughts. Not long before, Sturm had entered the following observation into the trench diary that he kept on quiet nights in the hours between sentry duty: "Since the discovery of morality and gun powder, the phrase 'the selection of the fittest' has lost ever more meaning for the individual. It's possible to trace precisely how its meaning has gradually moved over to the state, which has been ever more ruthlessly confining the functions of the individual to a specialized sphere. Today and for a long time past, one is no longer valued at what one is truly worth in and of oneself, but rather only at what one is worth in relation to the state. Through this systematic process of elimination of a whole series of values worthwhile in and of themselves, men have been created who are no longer capable of living on their own. The primal State, as the sum of nearly equal strengths, still possessed the regenerative properties of simple organisms: If it were divided, the individual components were little damaged. They soon found new opportunities for combination and easily located their physical poles in their leader, their psychical poles in the priest or magician.

A severe injury to the modern state, on the other hand, threatens every individual in his existence—at least those who don't live directly from the land, which means the vast majority. From this massive danger naturally arises the embittered fury, the breathless "to the bitter end" of warfare that two such power structures wage with one another. In such clashes, it's no longer the abilities of the individual that are weighed against one another, as in the times of swords and spears, but rather those of the great organisms. Production, the state of technology, chemistry, educational systems, and railway networks: these are the powers that invisibly battle behind the billowing smoke clouds of mechanized warfare."

Sturm recalled these thoughts as he stood before the dead man. Here yet again an individual had emphatically protested against the slaveholding of the modern state. The state, however, an untrammeled idol, stomped over him and away.

The force that subordinated the life of the individual to an immovable will stood forth here in terrible clarity. War played out on a gigantic scale, before which the fate of the individual disappeared. The vastness and deadly desolation of the field, the long-distance operation of steel machines, and the relay of every movement in the night drew an unyielding Titan's mask over the proceedings. You moved toward death without seeing it; you were hit without knowing where the shot came from. Long since had the precision shooting of the trained marksman, the direct fire of guns, and with it the charm of the duel, given way to the concentrated fire of mechanized weapons. The outcome was a game of numbers: Whoever could cover a certain number of square meters with the greater mass of artillery fire, won. Battle was a brutal confrontation of mass forces, a bloody struggle of production and materiel.

For this reason, too, the warriors, these underground servants of murderous machines, often went for weeks without realizing that men fought here against men. A cloud of smoke that swirled too early in the dawn; a clod of earth that an unseen arm threw out across the way from under cover; a muffled call that the wind carried over—that was all that offered itself to the watchful senses. It was understandable, then, that someone who was pummeled in this wasteland for years would be overcome by horror. It was at base the same feeling of meaninglessness that was sometimes evoked in a melancholy mind by the barren housing blocks of factory towns—that feeling with which mass oppressed the soul. And just as there one hurriedly strode to the city center in order to disperse gloomy thoughts among cafés, mirrors, and lights, so one sought here to escape oneself in conversations, in drink, and in peculiar detours of the brain.

2

Every society formed of men dependent on one another develops according to the laws of organic nature. It's generated from the fusion of different seeds and grows from there like a tree, which owes its characteristics to a series of conditions. The first encounter is a fundamentally hostile one: Men slink around one another, masked; each one presents himself as he wants to be seen, and spies out the weak points of the other. Gradually, sympathies come into play; shared antipathies and passions are discovered. Common experiences and intoxications disrupt the boundaries separating them, and finally the society is like a house that one has visited on many occasions: One has a clear mental picture of it and holds it in remembrance.

The remarkable thing is that this process actually brings about an alteration of the personality. Everyone will have observed in himself that he's a different person in this circle as opposed to that one. Just as marriage makes a couple more similar with time, so does every long-lived community alter its members fundamentally.

The three platoon leaders of the third company had been influenced in this way by one another. After the period of mobile warfare, which had bound them together merely as soldiers and comrades, they had discovered one another as personalities. They had emerged after the last open battle at the vanguard of their platoons, as Lieutenant Döhring, Sergeant Hugershoff, and Ensign Sturm. They maintained these positions in the following long period of trench warfare; in the course of time, the latter two were also made officers. Temporarily spared by the fortunes of war, they banded ever more closely together, like men united by a stay on a desert island.

Gradually they developed the need to spend the afternoons together. If they were in the trenches, they met in Sturm's dugout. When they were off-duty, they visited one another in quarters and, used to a nighttime existence, tended to extend these visits until morning. And so, without realizing it, they grew together into a pronounced spiritual union.

In addition to the events of the day, a common literary interest formed the basis of their conversation. Their reading habits were broad, as was typical for the literary youth of Germany. Common to all of them was a primitive leaning, which blended together in a strange way with a certain decadence. They liked to trace it back to the influence of the war, which had burst forth like an atavistic spring on the plains of a late, luxuriant culture. So for example they shared a distinct taste for phenomena as disparate in time, space, and meaning as Juvenal, Rabelais, Li-tai-pe, Balzac, and Huysmans. Sturm once defined this taste as joy in the scent of evil from the primeval forests of power.

Döhring, the oldest, was a cavalry reserve officer and an administrative lawyer; every other interest seemed more important to him, however, than that of his profession. He possessed a wonderful, pleasing way of dealing in superfices and used to call sincerity the surest way of making oneself unpopular. If he thought it was worthwhile to be known better, as he did here, it soon became clear that his glib exterior was the product of careful maintenance, and that he was actually quite capable of taking in fine and complex things. These, too, he grasped surely and easily, from an inborn joy in form. It gave him pleasure to adopt a foreign style that he soon let drop again. So he sometimes pronounced his sentences in archaic bureaucratic German; laid them on thick and full of color, like a storyteller in an Arab coffeehouse; or spat them out "expressionistically"— and the two others cheerfully played along.

Hugershoff, the painter, had been surprised by the outbreak of war while on a trip to Rome. When in a bad mood, which occurred ever more frequently these days, he used to curse the fact that he had returned. While he was off-duty he sometimes painted; after one art-critical discussion with Döhring that led to a quarrel, they had tacitly agreed never to discuss his paintings again. He called himself a pure colorist, which was true insofar as one could recognize nothing in his paintings apart from the colors. He identified ecstasy as the true essence of his art. Sturm recalled how he expressed himself in those days: "When I need a white highlight, then I slap it down; if I have no brush at hand, then I use the first thing I find, even if it's an old herring-head. Just look at a Rembrandt: There might be a layer of sky, a strip of forest, and a meadow in the foreground; you can hang it upside down on the wall, and you'll still be powerfully affected by it." Döhring had replied that it wasn't exactly the point of a Rembrandt to be hung upside down on the wall, and that he could hardly think of two things less similar than ecstasy and a herring-head. That had been the cause of the quarrel. Otherwise, Hugershoff was an easygoing companion; he could bear contradiction in all other areas. As a wild eroticist he knew how to incorporate even the most abstract word into a salacious joke. In order to keep such distractions in check, they had agreed to confine this theme to the first half hour of every get-together. This half hour always resembled a historical, ethnographic, literary, pathological, and personal curiosity cabinet. Hugershoff, who was master of erotic literature from the *Kama Sutra* and Petronius to Beardsley, found himself in his element here. He was in addition an exemplary battle officer, well versed in all technical and tactical questions.

Strangely enough, Sturm, the youngest, exerted the strongest influence in this small circle. Before the war he had been studying zoology in Heidelberg and had suddenly enlisted—out of temporary insanity, as Döhring would say. At base, though, it was the dichotomy between the equally highly evolved active and contemplative halves of his nature that had led him to this step. He was valued by his superiors as a quiet, trustworthy resource; as a man he was popular, though in a different way from Döhring. In battle he was brave—not from an excess of enthusiasm or conviction, but from a fine feeling of honor that rejected the faintest impulse toward cowardice as something unclean. In his free time he pursued a wide-ranging correspondence, read much, and also wrote. This activity was followed by the others with great attentiveness. The most captivating thing about him was that he could abstract from the events of the day to an unusual degree. And so he gave his friends through contact with him that which they unconsciously sought in drink and in their literary and erotic conversations: escape from the present.

3

On the day of the morning on which he had encountered the young suicide, Sturm sat in his dugout and wrote. The dugout was actually a small cellar that had remained intact beneath the rubble of a shelled house. A year earlier Sturm had had the debris reinforced through a double layer of sandbags and believed himself to be thereby sheltered from the impact of smaller and mid-sized shells. The entry led through the free-standing archway of the onetime entrance of the house; the name of the owner, Jean Cordonnier, was still legible above it. Because this arch stood above the level of the trenches, it had been hidden from sight by a series of gray linen rags stretched before it. A short, winding stone staircase led from there directly into the barrel-vaulted cellar that Sturm inhabited. It had served in peacetime as a wine cellar, as evidenced by a heap of old barrel hoops and a small chimney, above which the wall was blackened up to the ceiling. Walls, floors, and ceiling were made from dark red brick, worn smooth and crumbling with age.

A narrow shaft cast a beam of light into the room, which cut a bright rectangle on a table pressed up against the wall. The background was lit indistinctly by a carbide lamp set in a niche. On the table a small, flat space cleared for writing was surrounded by books and a jumble of objects. On an open map, scattered with red and blue symbols, sat an instrument for measuring distances, a compass, and a large army pistol. Jutting forth from the bisected brass casing of a 15-cm. cartridge stood three short, blackened tobacco pipes; next to it lay a leather pouch full of shag tobacco. Near the wall stood a seltzer bottle full of red-brown moonshine and a squat wine glass into which were etched flowers and the following inscription: "Des verres et des jeunes filles sont toujours en danger."[1] The

1. "Glasses and young girls are always in danger."

books were stacked precariously atop one another; many signs betrayed the fact that the owner read them simultaneously, in snatches. One lay open: an old edition, bound in pig leather, of *Veneres et Priapi uti observantur in gemmis antiquis*,[2] by the learned adventurer Dancarville. On the page opposite the title engraving stood the following: "To Sturm, from Hugershoff—a memento." Among others there were Vaerst's *Gastrosophy* and *The Fine Cuisine of Stettin* from the year 1747.

For furniture, apart from the table, there were three old armchairs cadged from the houses of the village, a small chest for foodstuffs, and a bed frame held together with chicken wire. The bedspread was folded back. Over the head of the bed, in a gap in the wall, a wedge of wood held the end of a burnt-down candle.

Weapons shimmered from the walls: a carbine, an infantry rifle, and a rifle with telescopic sight. At the entrance to the stairs, a long wire held a series of hand grenades, hung thickly together like herrings. Above them on a shelf were stacked cartons full of white and colored flares. At eye level there was an unfinished frieze of mammoths and elk in the style of the Cro-Magnons, which Sturm had painted during the long rainy season of the previous autumn, using phosphorous paint meant for making signs in the trenches, and which Hugershoff had perfected with an ungainly portrait of the Venus of Willensdorf. Close to the light shaft hung a miniaturized reproduction of Hobbema's *Allee*, framed in antique-gold-finished rosewood. Sturm had brought it back with him from his first leave home; he especially prized this work because he had come to know the landscape it depicted, almost unaltered and with the same color tones, during battle in Flanders. When in the evening a last beam of sunlight streamed through the shaft, blue-gray tobacco smoke swirling through it, a quiet golden glow emanated from

2. Work of erotic art by Pierre d'Hancarville (1719–1805).

this masterpiece that reached the furthest corner of the desolate cellar.

Sturm was in a bad mood today. It must have been a result of the day's first sad impression. He had had the body of the dead man wrapped in a tarp and carried through the communications trench to the village. Then he had strolled through his platoon sector and followed the course of the entrenchments. Everything technical was anathema to him, and yet the field fortifications, which made a complex battle site out of an innocuous piece of nature, fascinated him more and more. He traced that reaction back to the influence of the war, which diverted all interests into simpler paths. One became more practical in this climate. Precisely because of the sharp contrast that it afforded, however, the few hours that one could dedicate here to spiritual pursuits allowed one to reach the pinnacle of pleasure.

Perhaps it was the clarity and certainty of these battle structures that gripped him so. He remembered how, on a street near the harbor of the northern German city where he was raised, he had often closely observed an ancient city tower, in whose windowless, powerful, foursquare structure only narrow arrow slits were cut.

This tower loomed as a threatening gesture over a mass of gables. From the frozen sea of competing architectural styles it alone rose forth as a closed and solid unity. Only war brought forth such manifestations. When at night Sturm strode among the gun emplacements on the traverse and saw behind each a well-armed figure on solitary watch, he had the same feeling every time: gigantic and fabulous. This feeling didn't rest on machine guns, massive artillery pieces, or the jumble of telephone wires. That was only the form, the transitory style, in which power manifested itself. The essence was completely untouched by it; it seemed to reside in the earth like an animal and circulated in the blood as mystery. It was like a musical tone or a scent, heavy with unnameable memories. It must surely have gripped all men of all lands and times in nights of battle.

When the sun had melted away the mist, Sturm crept into the abandoned communications trench immediately before the front line and lay in wait in his old spot, which he called the "blind," carrying a rifle with a telescopic sight. The communications trench consisted only of a shallow, sun-hardened trough that wound through the ravaged meadows. When at midday no-man's-land flickered in the hot glare of the sun, a stupefying scent of fermenting earth and essential floral oils stagnated in the trough. The flora of the landscape had become strangely altered, since scythes no longer cut it. Sturm had observed how many of the plants that had until then led a barely tolerated existence in empty lots and the verges of roads had gradually assumed possession of the wide open spaces, where here and there harvest equipment still moldered like an extinct species of animal. A different smell, hotter and wilder, lay over the fields now. And the animal world had undergone a similar transformation. The crested lark, for example, had completely disappeared, now that garden paths only distinguished themselves from the landscape as long bands overgrown with greenery; the field larks, on the other hand, had increased incredibly in number. When the morning showed as a first silver streak on the eastern horizon, their trills spanned the field like a single melody. The white butterflies and swallowtails swayed only over the ruined walls of the village, while their caterpillars found sustenance in the cabbage plants and carrots of gardens gone to seed. Clouds of thistle-butterflies, on the other hand, hovered around the lightning-blue blossoms; silver-flecked gossamer-winged butterflies and the scarce coppers that are inseparable from them played around the green puddles of water that had formed in shell craters. Moles had become less common, since the ground had become more compacted and full of roots; at the same time, swarms of large, stinking rats settled in the trenches and the cellars of the village. When one walked to one's post at night on streets overgrown with grass, they scuttled ahead in noiseless packs.

Man had done all of that. In his soul a change occurred, and the landscape received a new face. Man was at the root of everything, yet this effect was so monumental that he sometimes failed to recognize his part in it. These nights in the wasteland, illuminated by flashes of lightning and dazzled by the uncertain shimmer of flares, gave a true reflection of his soul. As he lay in his blind, Sturm recognized that he, too, had become a different man. The man who lay here behind a stand of thistle and watched for prey over the sight of his rifle was not the same man who two years earlier had walked matter-of-factly down the tumultuous streets and who knew every last detail of the big city like the back of his hand. What had possessed him back then—him, the man of books and coffeehouses, the intellectual with the nervous appearance? What had thrust him into the army, in the midst of work on his doctorate? It was the war, which he had carried in his blood like any other real son of his time, long before, a fiery beast, he entered the actual arena. For the intellect had become too refined; it sprang like a tightrope walker back and forth between unbridgeable contradictions. How much longer before it disappeared into an abyss of insane laughter? The mysterious pendulum that resides in everything alive, that ineffable world-reason, had suddenly swung to the other side and sought with the might of a fist, with the force of a tremendous explosion, to force a breach through the brittle masonry and open the way to new paths. And a generation, a wave in the sea, called it nonsense, because they were destroyed by it.

Above all, one lived these days more acutely through the senses. That was already clear from the sound of one's breath as one lay in wait for the enemy. At those moments one was nothing more than tensed muscle, eye, and ear. Who could have imagined such feelings even two years earlier? What stood behind it? The fatherland? Sturm, too, had been caught up in the delirium of 1914; it was only when his intellect began to abstract the idea of the fatherland that he could perceive the driving force in its full might. He had long since come to see ordinary soldiers as lovers, all of whom swore fidelity to a single beloved, without realizing that they were all possessed by the same love.

Today, again, the unbelievable had happened. He had lain motionless for an hour in his stifling ditch, nothing in his sight but a sharp bend in the long, narrow line of the horizon that showed itself across the pasture. There was a spot there, where, every two hours, for a few seconds, one could see the relief of an English sentry post. Yes—this time, too, he had not waited in vain; just now something yellow had streaked above the crest of the earthworks: the incoming sentry—now the relieved sentry would have to pass the same spot. Sturm re-checked the sight, released the safety catch, and readied himself. There it was—a head under a flat, green-gray helmet and a piece of shoulder, topped by the muzzle of the rifle slung on it. Sturm hesitated, as the head paused in the crosshairs of his sight....

The countryside lay quiet and dead once again; only the white umbels of the hemlock trembled in the glare. Had he hit his target? He didn't know. But whether the man across the way now colored the clay of the trench floor red or not was not the question. The astonishing thing was that he, Sturm, had just now tried to kill another man, coldly, clearly, and absolutely deliberately. And once again the question recurred: Was he the same man as a year ago? The man who a short time before had been writing a PhD thesis entitled "On the Propagation of the *Amoeba Proteus* through Artificial Division"? Was there a more stark contrast possible than that between a man who lovingly lost himself in observing a fluid life force clustered around a tiny nucleus, and a man who cold-bloodedly shot at the most highly evolved life form? For the man over there could as easily have studied at Oxford as he had at Heidelberg. Yes, he had become a completely different man, different not only in deed but—and this was the essential thing—in feeling. The fact that he felt no remorse but rather satisfaction indicated a profoundly transformed morality. And the same held true for countless others who crept along the immeasurable lengths of the front. In striding through an ancient experience, a new race gave rise here to a new conception of the world. This war was a primeval mist of psychic possibilities, laden with modern attributes; whoever recognized only the raw and barbaric in its influence selected a single attribute out of a gigantic complex with precisely the same ideological arbitrariness as those who saw in it only the patriotic-heroic.

After this interlude Sturm crept back into the battle trenches and, on the way back to his dugout, called out to every orderly and off-duty sentry he passed, "I just offed another one." He watched their faces carefully; not one among them failed to smile approvingly. Kettler, the boy who brought his meals, had already heard about it in the trenches and congratulated him. Sturm had a kind of bond of trust with him. Kettler had dug himself a trench near the cellar steps in which he lived and slept. In heavier bombardments, Sturm used to crawl over to him, as he didn't have complete faith in the bomb-proof nature of his sandbags. They had for this reason passed many hours in conversation already.

Kettler was what one usually called a "simple man," but Sturm knew that at base there were no simple men. Naturally there were those who responded the same way to the same things as many others, but they were for this reason still by no means easy to understand for those who responded differently. Sturm tried, in getting to know Kettler, to open a window into the soul of the masses, in the midst of whom circumstances forced him to live. This manner of observation, in which he drew objective conclusions about the general from the particular, came naturally to him as a result of his scientific education.

He considered it most important, in his relationship with Kettler, to become fluent in the language of the common man. For this was clear to him: whoever couldn't talk their language couldn't reach them. He had seen that during visits to the front lines by the general staff officers. There were certainly extraordinary intellects among them, men who knew much more than the rudiments of their craft—yet Sturm had the distinct impression that they didn't know how to talk to the men. Their conversations seemed to him like the exchange of tokens, behind which the two parties saw completely different values: The words passed through smooth slabs of ice and lost their warmth as they did so. Despite the best will in the world, there was a deep cleft between them. A hundred years before it had been easier; worldviews that had grown from the same soil had united noble officers and enlisted boys from the country. These days, in the academically trained army officers and the reserve recruits from the factories, two alien worlds stood in opposition to one another. Even the hastily called up student and the man of the people stood very far apart. Before the war there had been so much written about the intellectual improvement of the officer corps that the basic human element had been forgotten—and that was the key thing in this occupation. Sturm thought about "Marshall Forward,"[3] "Papa Wrangel,"[4]

3. In the original, "Marschall Vorwärts," a nickname for Gebhard Leberecht von Blücher (1742–1819), a Prussian field marshal who fought with the Duke of Wellington against Napoleon I at the Battle of Waterloo in 1815.

4. Friedrich Heinrich Ernst Graf von Wrangel (1784–1877), another field marshal of the Prussian Army.

and a series of generals of the first empire who, though intellectually not exceptional, achieved splendid things. That was due above all to the fact that they understood their people and had mastered their language to its smallest details. These men had deeply penetrated the souls of the men they led, and that was more important than the mechanical understanding of the first-class general staff officer, who loomed over the masses, in isolation, as a pure, cultivated intellect.

Of course one had to admit that circumstances were different today. The distances alone made closer connections impossible. And also relevant here was the fact that it wasn't any longer an organ of the state but the state as a whole that engaged in war. The more powers that were engaged, the bigger the tensions and contradictions had to be. Since the higher leadership could no longer oversee the battlefield, they naturally evolved to greater degrees of specialization; the human element became the responsibility of the lesser leadership. But there was always the looming danger that the masses didn't fully understand the common goal. And weak points wouldn't long sustain a body put to the test of a long war.

Above all it was misguided to expect the masses to consciously subordinate their way of life for long to an ideal. That was the same as asking fishermen to live on land. When Blücher had called out to the troops on the march to Waterloo, "I promised it to my friend Wellington," he had cloaked the task in a formula that even the last musketeer could understand. Today words like "persevere" and "hero's death" had been so ceaselessly bandied about that they had long since acquired an ironic sound—at least wherever there was actual fighting. Why didn't they invent slogans today like "A manor for every front-line soldier"? Once, before an attack, Sturm had heard an old sergeant say the following: "Kids, we're going over there now to gobble up the Englishmen's rations." It was the best battle address that he had ever heard. That was surely something good in the war—that it destroyed glorious-sounding phrases. Concepts that hung fleshless in the void were overcome by laughter.

Every idea needed a stable foundation—that one couldn't overlook. What would have become of Christianity if it were not for the masses' misunderstanding of its social ideals? The French Revolution had become a reality through the word "freedom," which the shining thoughts of a few minds and the starvation of many bodies had united in deeds. Today it was "persevere." In that word some saw the will to battle, while others saw the fact that there was too little to eat. That's why the slogan of the old sergeant carried greater weight.

The meal that Kettler brought, which Sturm spooned up out of an aluminum tin, occasioned this train of thought. It was gray-green stuff that the cooks called dehydrated vegetables and the men called barbed wire, which had at first appeared infrequently as an island in the flood of peas, noodles, and beans, but which had for a long while now been the only dish on the bill of fare. Meager fibers of red-brown beef and slimy cubes of potato swam in it. The meat had "cooked down," as usual. Sturm often found matchstick- or thread-like stems in his mouth, which he spat out with a powerful curse onto the brick floor. The rats, too, had to live. But the problem of the rations was truly bad; even the best editorials couldn't get around it. And it was the so-called simple man, whose life was so intimately bound to his musculature, who was hit particularly hard by it. When one deprived him, as here, of women, food, and sleep, then he had almost nothing left.

"In such wastelands, the man of the contemplative life fares better," thought Sturm, as he placed the mess tin on the ground, dug through his papers, and finally pulled out a sheet half-covered in writing. "One could look at current events with the eyes of the Middle Ages: then one has the castles' clash of arms and monastic isolation, is warrior and monk at the same time. At base, every man experiences his own war. It stands to reason that a Börries von Münchhausen[5] or a Löns,[6] who died in this regiment, navigates it differently than a Lotz[7] or a Trakl."[8]

It was a peculiar collision of forces that drove Sturm to write during this time. As a student he had flirted with the bohemian life, writing short, Baudelaire-influenced pieces of art criticism for befriended painters, and submitting contributions to those newspapers that from time to time sprang up like brave flowers in the detritus of the big cities, only to wither away again after three numbers because no one read them. As a cadet and ensign he had hardly thought about those days. Yet precisely here, in the midst of heightened activity, the need to write awoke again.

The contradictory pull of his passions, which threw him as between two women from one embrace into the other, made Sturm unhappy. He had rather seen himself either as a pure man of action, who only used his brain as a means to an end, or as a thinker, to whom the exterior world was only meaningful as a source of contemplation.

At the time he was writing a series of novellas, in which he attempted to capture on paper the latest form of mankind in its finest emanations. He would gladly have gathered his powers in a novel, but it seemed too early for him yet, in this witches'

5. Börries Freiherr von Münchhausen (1874-1945) was a German poet who served in World War I and was later closely associated with the Nazi regime.

6. Hermann Löns (1866-1914) was a German journalist and writer who died, three weeks after enlisting, while on patrol with the 73rd Fusilier Regiment near Reims.

7. Ernst Wilhelm Lotz (1890-1914) was a German Expressionist poet who died near Bouconville, France, during a raid on a French entrenchment.

8. Georg Trakl (1887-1914) was an Austrian Expressionist poet who served in a medical capacity in World War I. Plagued by depression, Trakl committed suicide by cocaine overdose while stationed near Krakow.

cauldron of apparitions. It was also an undertaking that couldn't be reconciled with a life full of commotion. So he had decided to develop a series of characters, each from its own center, in tightly unified passages. He planned to combine them with a title that would express the commonalities of their time—disquiet, obsession, and feverish intensity.

Today he had hardly grasped his pencil before he heard Döhring and Hugershoff groping their way down the stairs. They had evidently already taken care of the first item on the usual afternoon agenda in Döhring's dugout, because, as they fell into their seats and laid their gas masks to the side, they resumed a conversation already begun in the trenches about the events of Verdun. It was the old debate, about whether to grab the bull by the horns or not.

Sturm always enjoyed their conversations. Hugershoff almost always parried with a sharply delineated, internally predetermined, vivid perspective. He drew in whatever cropped up in the conversation and ordered it under this perspective. He built his sentences squarely one on top of the other into a structure in which he sat so securely that he was impossible to drive out. Döhring, on the other hand, obviously placed more value on the polished form of the word than on the outcome of the conversation. He changed his position at whim and nimbly leapt at his opponent from the most varied perspectives. At the same time, he by no means remained on the surface; he dazzled, without being a *causeur.*[9] Yet he only used these methods with those he valued; with others, he wholeheartedly adopted his opponent's position, thereby nipping in the bud any possibility of an unpleasant or pointless conflict. Sturm had adopted this habit from him and found it exceptionally practical.

9. One who talks fluently or much; the connotation can be derogatory, as of one who speaks indiscreetly and speaks ill of others.

Naturally they shortly came to discuss the operational outlook for the near future. The quagmire of Verdun had brought both sides to a halt; already, though, another storm loomed on the horizon. The prospects couldn't be too bright at this stretch of the front, either, or the regiment would have long since been transferred to Verdun; it had already been in the same spot for over a year. Many small signs betrayed the fact that the quiet that had reigned here so long was illusory. The opposing forces were quite openly arming themselves for an offensive, whose left flank would have to break off at approximately this point. They used to see no aircraft for weeks on end; now, aerial barrages were flown from dawn until dusk. The firing patterns of the artillery, too, had become very suspicious. Different targets were continually being chosen and covered with two or three rounds. That made an unremarkable, almost random impression. Yet the artillery survey and sound-ranging sections insisted that almost every round came from a different battery position. In nights with no wind the rattling of faraway munitions trucks filled the air. Döhring told how during his watch on the previous night he had heard a fine, ceaseless hammering noise, metal striking metal. Were they mounting gun emplacements in their trenches? Installing gas cylinders?

They took strange pleasure in discussing what was to come, though it might already be looming over them like an invisible wave. Beneath the crest of impending events it seemed to them a peculiar kind of bravery to weigh the possibilities. Danger lay so close, so palpable, that they only dared speak of it in whispers. For this was certain: when whatever was preparing itself now actually broke loose, hardly any of them would live through it. On the other side, thousands, perhaps, were ready to spring, and the guns were directing their sights toward their targets. A powerful, stupefying scent, like flowering meadows in August, enshrouded this life under the mouths of the cannons. Here, in this island of culture in the midst of the threatening devastation, awoke a feeling that enveloped every culture before its decline with the shimmer of a last and highest luxuriousness: the feeling of total superfluity, of an existence that for a short time stands like fireworks above night-darkened waters.

Döhring expressed this feeling by saying, in closing: "Our situation reminds me of that of the crew of Sinbad the sailor, who joyfully landed on the back of a monstrous fish, pitched tents, and gathered around a fire. Hopefully we, too, will have the equanimity to shout 'Allah il Allah' when it plunges us into the depths. I propose that, as best our meager means allow, we live in the meantime like the Romans, who embraced life to the fullest one last time before opening their veins. In doing so, they exhibited at once two virtues that all real men combine: the love of life and contempt for death. Let's pass the bottle around one more time, smoke a pipe, and listen to what Sturm has to read for us."

"Please help yourselves to the bottle, the tobacco, and my pipe collection," answered Sturm, "and I'll attempt to make a late city-dweller appear on the pavement before you. These are of course only the first brushstrokes of a portrait I began yesterday; however, I'll let you share in the latest developments."

He began to read:

4

"One forenoon in early autumn, Tronck strolled along his usual route over the streets of the big city. It was one of those rare mornings in the year in which, with barely perceptible shadings, a hint of decay underlay high summer's strength—one of those mornings on which one decides to replace one's plain jacket that evening with a subtly patterned between-seasons coat. The trees on the avenues and grassy places still stretched overhead in their steel-green armor: They displayed one last onslaught of green, polished by the previous day's rain to a metallic sheen. Of course, here and there a drop of yellow or a spark of red was already sprayed through the mass of foliage, and from time to time a leaf spotted or edged in flame circled slowly to the asphalt. Whether a gust of wind from a streetcar or the stroke of a bird's wing had plucked it—one sensed the heaviness that dreamed in the leaves and lured them to the earth: The power that had driven this luxuriance from roots to tips was exhausted and anxious to complete its cycle. The boundaries that distinguished color and form from one another were somewhat blurred; the air was disturbed by light precipitation. This misting was not yet denser than the cloud made by a drop of milk in a glass of water, yet in its scent there already lay the announcement of the fleet of fog that autumn held in wait. It was one of those transformations in progress, barely perceived by the senses, that raised fleeting feelings of lust or sadness from the depths of the soul.

"Tronck, who always surrendered to the subtlest moods, perceived these small imperfections as he would the first line at the corner of an eye or the first white hair on the head of a beautiful woman: as a compulsion to love once more, to embrace once more, before evening came. He was like a soldier before battle, when the signal fires crackle in the twilight—bound to life; at once melancholy and strong.

"Outwardly he appeared polished and detached, a thirty-year-old who saw his calling in an elegant appearance. Although he was unremarkably dressed, he drew the glances of the crowd that characterized the streetscape around this time. Loafers, pensioners, and retirees passed slowly by, and sometimes also a serving girl in a pink- or blue-striped blouse, from whom one could smell from afar the powerful scent of soap. Bank clerks with black cases under their arms seemed to have a great deal of time; they stretched a walk to the post office into a morning's promenade. The representatives of the propertied classes made haste; business dealings hied them from office to office; calculations twitched in their features. Further along, young girls in black aprons stood in front of shops and appraised from outside the effect of their window decorations. If they hadn't placed their left hands on their hips just so and stroked their hair with their right, one might almost have believed that they were serious in their task.

"These people all grazed Tronck, who hardly noticed them, with their glances. All of them had the same impression in doing so, which was converted in each into a different emotion. The bank clerks admired him, then convinced themselves that it was merely a question of dress; as they walked further, they lost themselves in capitalist daydreams of the future. The bourgeois were visibly disturbed; they smoothed their trouser creases and regained their equilibrium only by meditating on a bank account or a hard-earned title.

"A good observer would recognize that Tronck dressed more for himself than for others. Neither color nor form was what struck one about him. His suit played in two soft tones of nutmeg brown, sharply defined at collar and cuffs by the white edges of his linen. All the colors he wore were defined in small gradations and muted contrasts. Pronounced was only the necktie, whose knot hovered like a shimmering butterfly over the polished stone that closed his shirtfront. As far as form went, which arose from the cut, fold, and drape—it would have been clear to the initiated that in this, the painstaking influence of an artist had given the craft of the tailor a higher meaning, and that individuality was expressed here within the bounds of fashion. In the shoes, too, a craftsmanship found expression that was hardly to be found anymore, since the title of the purveyor to the court had been ground down by the laughter of the badly dressed masses.

"A man used to judging externalities correctly—that is, as an expression of the internal—would have judged Tronck's appearance as a peculiar mixture of freedom and constraint. There was something of the priest or the officer in it, something strict and uniform, but it was shot through and ameliorated with a certain artistic ease. It was the dress of a man who subordinated himself to the rules and laws of a particular social circle out of a longing for form, although he stood spiritually superior to it.

"Superiority also shone in his face—energy and intellect together. It was a fine, pale face, thoughts playing over it during the walk. Its bearer strode through the crowd with the confidence of the native city-dweller, who walked like a sleepwalker past all obstacles, while his spirit traveled completely different paths." — — —

Sturm stopped and with his pencil scribbled in the margins a few words that had evidently occurred to him as he read. Then he asked, as he stuffed a pipe: "What do you think about the beginning?"

"I must admit," said Hugershoff, "that his appearance strikes me as remarkably familiar. You've begun with a carefully painted portrait; how do you plan to develop it?"

"That's not easy to answer. You might remember the outrage with which Baudelaire describes having seen in an atelier a cleanly sketched, quartered canvas on which the painter laboriously added paint, bit by bit, working from a single corner. I must say, that this method is equally distasteful to me in writing.

"Of course, every plot emerges from a problem. In this case I intend to explore the tension between the drive for action in a singular man and the constraint placed on this drive by the frame in which his environment fixes him. How little the actual material matters to me you'll see in the fact that it's still not clear to me whether I'll let this Tronck individual play in the cage of the bohemian or in the civil service. What's important to me is only that his being subordinates itself completely to a pattern.

"Observation of our small community here actually awoke these trains of thought in me. Before the war, all three of us had a worldview that somehow extended beyond the national. We read more than just the German newspapers in the coffeehouses and overstepped the boundaries of the country in more than just a geographical sense. Yet at the same time it wasn't compulsion that drove us to follow our flag, as the world arranged itself into warring camps. You, for example, could have stopped in Geneva or Zürich on your way back and watched the drama from afar, without changing your previous lifestyle. How many of our literati sit there even now! But that is the great difference between them and us—they observe and write, while we act. They've lost the connection, while in us the great rhythm of life vibrates. Which flag one stands behind is all the same in the end, but this is certain: The last *Feldgraue* or the last *Poilu*[10] who fired and loaded at the Marne is of greater importance to the world than all the books the literati can heap up.

"We, too, try to gain a broader view of our time, but we do it from the center, while they do so from the periphery. We have subordinated ourselves to the progress of a great, necessary event; our own will—that which we call freedom or personality—often stands in contradiction to it. And that which we try to accomplish on this miserable piece of ground—the free unfolding of the personality in the midst of the most stringent constraints that one can imagine—is what I'd like to bring to full expression in the person of Tronck."

10. Slang, respectively, for German and French soldiers: *Feldgraue* refers to the gray color of the German uniform, and *Poilu* means, literally, "hairy one," referring to the mustaches and beards of many of the country-bred French soldiers.

"I'd like to warn you, though," Döhring interjected, "against getting enmeshed too deeply in trivialities. Anyone looking at the books that you seem to prefer these days could take you for a cook, a gemstone dealer, or a modern parfumeur. That you read Vaerst's *Gastrosophy* is understandable, but with *The Fine Cuisine of Stettin* you begin to lose yourself in irrelevancy."

Sturm had become thoughtful. "I'd like to remind you of the words you spoke earlier about the Romans. Imagine that someone condemned to death who had been sitting for months in a desolate cell were given a bouquet of flowers. Wouldn't he take special, deep pleasure in every color, every petal, and every stamen? Observe how Wilde extols the sliver of heaven visible to the inmates through the shaft in the wall of the Reading jail. It is precisely then, when life is threatened, that it strives to connect with as much as possible; it sends out light and radio signals like a sinking ship. At such times a man is like a miser who rummages through his treasures one last time before death. I believe that our literature will reflect this obsession with the multifarious. It is the flight of the artist from a heroic age."

"So that's the reason that you hardly touch on the war?" asked Hugershoff.

"I tried it twice. But in doing so I realized that everything in it that goes beyond the actual is distasteful to me. I live too deeply in it to be able to observe it as an artist. It might be possible for me in five years. Reflection requires detachment."

5

Sturm had barely uttered the last word when a furious crash convulsed the countryside. It was as if a series of thunderbolts had nested themselves inside one another, in an effort to exceed themselves in fury. A series of impacts roared out, one after another, so quickly that the consciousness melded them into a single, terrible phenomenon. The arches of the cellar swayed;

fissures tore through the ceiling; fine brick powder filled the air and made breathing difficult. The glass from the shaft in the wall was shattered all over the table; sharp, suffocating blasts of air burst into the room and blew out the flame from the carbide lamp. At the same time, corrosive clouds of smoke swirled through the stairwell and the shaft in the wall. Their nerves trembled at perceiving the familiar smell of an explosion, which the impact of countless shells had cemented into their memories.

One voice rang out: "Attack, attack, out!" And in between: "Kettler, my gas mask! For God's sake, pass me the hand grenades!" Then all the inhabitants of the cellar lurched outside.

When Sturm gained the open air and worked his way through a stretch of the communications trench to the front line, he found himself swathed in blue-white clouds of vapor. All kinds of light signals hung in the air: white magnesium lights, red barrage commands, green signals for regulating artillery fire. The enemy seemed to be working with trench mortars; the heavy, tearing impacts didn't sound like artillery fire. An unbroken shower of clods of earth rattled down on the trench; small pieces of steel hissed like hailstorm through the muffled din. Then an iron bird flew to the earth, spiraling wider and wider; Sturm just had time to spring into a ditch, before a blast of fire threw him like a sack against the exposed clay wall. The assault was of a scale that exceeded the power of hearing; Sturm could only perceive the plummeting fountains of fire with his eyes. They were hardly extinguished, before they flared up again. Sturm pressed himself tightly into a hole that a grenade must have made in the trench wall: The inner layer of clay was burnt black and sprayed with yellow-brown flecks of picric acid. He saw this pattern clearly with that sharpness of perception that directed itself in such situations toward the most inconsequential things. Every time material rained down on him, he flung his hands before his eyes, completely aware as he did so that he was doing something senseless—if fate sent a piece of shrapnel into this hollow, his pitiful arms would provide him no protection. The whirring steel had such force that it could pierce not only his hand, but his eye and his skull as well. Nevertheless, he made the same gesture every time and felt relieved in doing so. Strangely, a bon mot of Casanova's came to mind each time, in which, wounded in the hand in a duel, he responded to a woman who asked why he hadn't hidden it behind his body: "I was much more anxious to hide my body behind my hand." The brain operated like a mad thing under the welling of the blood; from time to time a completely ridiculous fragment of thought was dashed to the surface.

In a passing moment of cold-bloodedness he remarked that he was sweating from anxiety. He tried to imagine how he looked: a trembling bundle in a torn uniform, with a blackened, sweat-streaked face and staring eyes in which fear could be read. He stood and tried to calm his nerves through a series of curses. He thought he had talked himself back into heroism, when a new and even more terrible impact hurled him back into his hole. A second that followed immediately upon the first broke off a huge piece of the trench wall and almost buried him. He writhed free from the mass of earth and ran along the trench. No man could be seen at his post. Once he stumbled over a heap of debris under which lay a dead body. Somehow, a long, jagged board had penetrated his body; his eyes, glassy and bulging, stood out of their sockets.

Finally, at the very flank of his company, Sturm encountered a non-com who stood ducked behind his machine gun. The man had not stood out much to him previously; he must have been one of those soldiers whom one first recognized in battle. He clapped him on the shoulder and offered him his hand. Then he pointed questioningly at the ground ahead; the man shook his head. Both of them laughed. It was a strange laughter, which distorted their faces. It was remarkable how calm Sturm was now. He positioned himself behind the machine gun and shot forward into the boiling smoke until steam hissed from the seams of the casing. Mortar shells still burst all around them; now, however, every explosion hammered the heart with the demand for stubborn resistance. Sturm had often noticed this in such moments: The individual was a weakling in times of danger. It was difficult, on the other hand, to be a coward when one was observed.

The firing finally stopped with the same suddenness with which it had begun. Only their own artillery still sent its hissing arcs over the field. The trenches came to life. The wounded were carried to the sanitation station—some cried out; others were pale and motionless. The group leaders sent reports; an orderly brought a note from Döhring:

"Company commander fallen; I've taken over command. Highest readiness for action overnight; further shelling and attack likely. A platoon of engineers en route for reinforcement. Report losses and requests for munitions to me. D."

Now Kettler came as well. He claimed to have been buried. Sturm acted as if he believed it. "I'm going to leave the platoon sector now. Call the group leaders together for orders at this traverse in fifteen minutes."

The trench was like a disturbed anthill. Everywhere people dragged boards and beams out of the way, shoveled caved-in spots free, and propped up the entrances of dugouts that had been hit. Many were pale and worked mechanically; others spoke quickly and excitedly. Next to a volunteer a mortar shell had fallen without exploding; he repeatedly related his evil impression of the projectile, which in his eyes seemed to be a living creature. A large piece of shrapnel had knocked the weapon from another man's hands. A third summed up his impressions with the following saying: "Times like that are pretty uncomfortable."

Sturm had to agree with him. The actual effect had been minimal: two dead and ten wounded, apart from the usual scratches and scrapes. Much worse was the psychic or, as the odd jargon had it, the moral effect. War technology had managed to give the idea of death such a dreadful expression in these mortar shells that artillery shells seemed by comparison harmless things. There was a terrible power in them paired with a kind of deceit. They strained all of the senses—even the one for air pressure, which must reside in the nasal passages—to the breaking point. Here, too, one could see the enhancement of human ability through technology: Compared to the roar of attack, the clash of weapons and hooves of an earlier time, these were thousands of times stronger. For that reason, the courage required here greatly exceeded that required of the Homeric heroes.

Twilight fell. Sturm strode slowly back through the churned-up earth of the trench. The posts were staffed now with helmeted men, who stood silent and motionless staring at the field before them. In the sky stood a small blue-green cloud, backlit by a rose-colored ray of the already sunken sun. The first flare shot high, giving the starting signal for a fiery ballgame of fear. From time to time the muted cry of a sentry rang out, at once subdued and uneasy. Then a burst of fire from a machine gun sprang forth like the scream with which a hysteric vents her nerves....

The section commanders stood at the designated traverse. They clicked their heels together. One reported: "Sergeant Reuter, officer on trench duty. Nothing new to report." Sturm took over:

"We have all seen how dangerous these mortar attacks can be. If the English advance under cover of such a firestorm, as is quite likely, they'll be in the trenches without encountering a single shot. For this reason the sentry posts can under no circumstances be left unmanned again. The company commander has ordered the highest state of alert for tonight. The rank and file will station themselves on the steps of the galleries, buckled up, rifles in their hands, hand grenades on their belts. Sentries will remain at their posts under fire. No exceptions. In case of attack, all will rush out and defend the posts. I'm making *you* responsible for your section. Your place is obviously on the uppermost step of the galleries. Retain constant contact with your sentries. Make it clear to your people that they'll be defenseless if they meet the enemy while still down below. The manning of the sentry posts is to be handled in the same way in every group. We have to view the peculiar circumstances of the battle as a kind of competitive task: In the few seconds available after the cessation of the barrage, it's up to the English to cover the distance between their trenches and ours, and for us, on the other hand, to get into firing position as quickly as possible. Whoever finishes first, wins. Try, then, to spread the barbed wire out as much as possible in front of your sections; the more obstacles the enemy finds, the more time we have. Reports will reach me temporarily in my dugout—in case of attack, in Reuter's group. I'd like to express special thanks to NCO Abelmann for courage under fire; after the relief I'll make an official report of it. Is everything clear, or does someone have a question?"

There followed a discussion of cease-fire signals, passwords, hand-grenade detonators, and similar matters. Then the group broke up. Sturm walked yet again the length of the trench. Before the entrance of every tunnel a group stood smoking. From time to time a sentence emerged: "Then every man hustles to his post and fires. Password Hamburg. The platoon commander is with Reuter's group." Everything seemed to be in order. Sturm returned to his dugout.

As he descended the steps, he had the feeling that he had not been there in a very long time. It had been hardly three hours since he'd left it, but the fine veil that time weaves had already interposed itself between him and it.

In the meantime Kettler had apparently busied himself in repairing the dugout. The window had been replaced by a piece of cardboard, and the carbide lamp burned on the table. Sturm lifted the bottle and took a long pull. Then he seated himself on the bed and lit a cigar. He shivered; the schnapps had not warmed him. It seemed strange to him that he sat here. How very close it had come to hitting him—to leaving him lying on the ground with stiffening limbs, like the corpse he had stumbled across in the trench—with large, senseless wounds in his body and a dirty, dark-blue, gunpowder-sprin-kled face. One second earlier, one meter farther—that had been decisive. It wasn't death that frightened him—that was a certainty—but rather the element of chance, the tumbling movement through time and space, which could descend any second into annihilation—this feeling of having worth and yet not being more than an ant that could be squashed in the street by the heedless step of a giant. Why, if there were a Creator, had he given men the desire to penetrate into the essence of a world that he could never fully fathom? Wouldn't it be better if men lived like animals or plants than always with this terrible anxiety lurking beneath the surface of everything that they said and did?

A vision emerged in the desert of his brain. He stood, ele-gantly dressed, in a large bookstore in the city of his birth. All around on the tables lay books; books were stacked up to the ceiling on enormous shelves, against which ladders leaned. The bindings were of leather, linen, silk, and parchment. The knowl-edge of all lands and all ages was crammed here in the narrowest of spaces. Here, too, large portfolios lay out, tied closed with ribbons. One need only untie the ribbons if one wanted to revel in old engravings and reproductions of beautiful paintings. On one stood, in gold lettering, *The Isenheim Altar*; on another, *The Green Passion*. He was in conversation with the bookseller, a young man with the chiseled face of an ascetic. Names of painters, philosophers, poets, dramatists, and famous novelists flew back and forth. Publishers, translations, layout, composition, and printings received expert appraisal. With every name blazed forth a hundred more, and each one was unparalleled in his art. It was a conversation between connoisseurs, experts who surveyed their domain. Their perspectives differed precisely to such an extent that every picture emerged as if stereoscopically. Their speech meshed like the parts of a precision-made machine; it played; it was like a precious object handed back and forth between lovers. The most wonderful thing was that it actually had no purpose, that it emerged only from the joy of being master in a completely clear element. And this spiritual pleasure was supported by a sensual one, in which one pulled a volume from the shelf, opened it, and stroked the binding and the pages with one's fingertips. Yes, he, Sturm, was happy today. He had strolled along the avenues of the city, on whose flagstones the fall had spread a broad mosaic of brown, red, and yellow leaves. The clear, moist air that made one's footsteps so light and crisp, the pure lines of the large buildings, the metallic outlines of the dying trees had filled him with the trembling and groundless joy that came over him from time to time. He stood standing a moment on an ancient bridge and saw a boy out fishing pull a long, gold-shimmering eel from the water. Under the light material of his suit, his blood beat warm and young beneath his skin. How meaningful was the smallest thing at such times. Wherever one's glance might fall, one's spirit connected everything to itself with the most beautiful and strange ideas. There were days on which one succeeded

at everything, on which power streamed from one as from a
charged battery. Then fate was no longer something uncertain
that lurked at the crossroads of life, but rather a colorful garden
whose gate one climbed and from which one lustily plucked
fruits and flowers. On such days one drew forth the utmost
of which one was capable. A certainty illuminated Sturm on
such days: Men living in earlier times had not known this wide
range of satisfactions, for the world of appearances had vastly
increased. One pronounced a word, a name—light as a breath
and yet of immeasurable weight. One named a figure of German Romanticism, of the Paris of 1850, of Russia after Gogol,
of Flanders after the Brothers van Eyck—and what a web of
associations one called forth. Every word was a tree that stood
on the roots of thousands of ideas—a light that the brain dif-
fracted into myriad lights. Yes, it was a great and godly gift,
that one could stand on a morning like this in the heart of a
great city and toss such words like diamonds into the sparkling
stream of conversation. In this place, surrounded by mahog-
any wood and shining mirrored glass, one felt oneself to be the
conscious and valuable son of a late age, heir to the completely
immeasurable treasures of the centuries. — — —

Steps came down the stairs. It was Döhring, accompanied by a strange officer. Sturm was glad that a human voice
cut through the stillness. Döhring seemed to be refreshed and
calm.

"That was a bit dodgy before; we were just about able to see
the potatoes from below. I want to move the company command center here; the dugout of poor Lieutenant Wendt was
rent to bits by one of the very first mortar shells. Wendt and
both of his orderlies were killed immediately. I just walked the
entire length of the trench again and saw that you already gave
the necessary orders. Hugershoff sends greetings; he's staying
on the left flank for the night. He has a monstrous bump on the

back of his head.—But excuse me—Lieutenant von Horn, commander of the engineering platoon—Lieutenant Sturm."

Both men bowed. They decided to hold watch together during the night. Kettler appeared from out of his cave, hacked apart the boards from a hand-grenade crate with his bayonet, and started a fire in the chimney. The bottle and the shell casing with the pipes was put out onto the table next to the carbide lamp and the chairs pushed up near the fire. A seasoned soldier, the Engineer had brought a bottle of rum with him. Kettler mixed its contents with some water in a cooking pot and hung it on a three-cornered French bayonet, which had been driven into the masonry of the chimney as a cooking pole. A strong scent of rum soon permeated the room; each man smoked and held a hot tin cup in his hand. The faces of the three men in the gray, clay-smeared uniforms were haggard and hollowed out by sharp contrasts in light and dark. Their shadows flickered in the play of the fire against the desolate walls, on which the luminescent paint of the antediluvian drawings phosphoresced. The conversation was crude, technical, and mercenary; it dealt with the experiences of war and of that which was to come.

The Engineer proved to be a man born for such situations. The simple and manly word, whose bearers sat so obscurely in the beer halls of the homeland, took on a bold, metallic sound here. Horn knew only the craft of weaponry, but *that*, he knew. Officers' family, cadet school, a small garrison on the western front, and then the war. He was one of those people for whom dealing with explosives was commonplace and the nightly encounter with the enemy par for the course—one of those people whom one can imagine only as a soldier. He had been one of the first to invade Lüttich, and in many waves of battle since then he had hurled himself with pistol and hand grenade into enemy trenches. When everything went south, he was in his element. Sturm wondered what would have become of such a man if the war had not broken out. He would have made one for himself—that's all there was to it. He would have trekked to Africa or China or died in some duel. Horn knew the front from the Alps to the sea, and related his experiences in an indifferent tone that lent an inimitable power to the terrible.

"Yes, gentlemen, Lens, that was a bad piece of work. It was there that I learned mining so well; day and night you stood on a volcano. Everywhere a web of coal mines under the front, and the Frenchman knew exactly where. Nearly every day a piece of the trench went up in the air; then you had to storm the hot crater while the shit still flew around your ears. Whoever got inside first, won. At the same time you always had to keep a lit cigar with you—we didn't have hand grenades with detonator pins in those days—only homemade ones that had a bit of fuse sticking out of one end. Maybe you know the ones I mean—they were casings that you filled with explosives, nails, and shards of glass.

"Below we sat, day shift and night, the demolition charge always at the ready. We often heard the enemy picks right next to us; then it was a matter of minutes, whether we crushed him or he us. I crouched in the hole sometimes with a microphone at my ear, waiting for the moment when the enemy would put their picks aside and start dragging in the cartons of dynamite. One time we just managed to light the fuse and get out of there. The explosion was so powerful that two men working in a communication trench three hundred meters away were killed by the concussion. The next day a funny thing happened. We were working in another place and suddenly broke open a huge hole in the wall. Before we knew what we'd done, someone over there shouted 'Qui vive?'—we had collided with French miners. Naturally we were immediately through the breach with pistols and knives. It was obviously a bit rough going—you could still smell the cigarette smoke, and you had a sense of dread that others lay in wait nearby.—You know those moments before the encounter when you curse the fact that you have to draw breath.

"Gentlemen, I once flew to the front for fun with an airman I'd befriended, in order to home in on a battery—we had the luck to be downed by a direct engine hit from an English flier. My friend broke all his bones; I didn't. I know my way around full-bore attacks and trench warfare—but all of that is child's play next to an encounter in a mineshaft. In those cases you have the feeling that you're already in your dug-out grave or already roasting in hell. The weight of the monstrous mass of earth surrounding you makes you feel completely abandoned, as if you'd never be found if you fell.

"Well, we laid ourselves down flat on the floor of the shaft and didn't move a muscle. Finally one of the enemy made the stupid mistake of firing. We jumped to our feet and laid him out, as well as a second man who also fired, grazing my skull.

"Then we followed the passage toward the enemy. Soon I felt a draft of air and a strange, shushing sound. When we were about a hundred meters from the source of the sound, it became clear to me that we had made a huge find. We had suspected for some time the existence of a vast underground workshop, fed by coal from the former coal mine, that supplied the French positions with light and drove the carts. It must have been the sound of this workshop that reached our ears. The draft was probably caused by a large ventilator that drew bad air from the mines.

"I drew a sketch by the light of a flashlight, and we crept back. After we dragged both corpses back to our side, we masked the hole with earth, so that it looked as if there had been a cave-in that had buried the miners. My captain, to whom I told the story, had a brilliant idea. He ordered a number of steel gas canisters from the engineering depot, which were hauled to the point of the collision that same night. In the morning we went there with listening apparatuses. We had called the artillery and asked them to shell the exit from the shaft at a designated hour. Below, we opened the hole once more and put canister after canister through, then set them off. It was naturally not dangerous at all for us, since the ventilator drew the gas very quickly. We could hear its humming very distinctly with our apparatuses.

"After a while, what we'd predicted would happen, happened: The noise stopped for a moment, and then started up again. The Frenchmen had turned the ventilator around and tried to drive the cloud of gas back toward us. We dammed the wall carefully back up and breakfasted in peace, the listening devices still at our ears. We heard the noise for about a quarter of an hour longer; then it became weaker, and finally everything was quiet. We learned later from prisoners' statements that we had smoked the entire garrison out like rats and polluted the entire network of tunnels for months. On top of that, the troops streaming out at the other end suffered severe losses from our artillery fire.

"Yes, at Lens, we really learned what war was all about. A few days before this happened..."

One experience gave way to the next. From time to time Kettler appeared and threw an armful of wood on the fire. When the cooking pot had been emptied, the Engineer disappeared for a time and returned with a filled canteen. He seemed to have provided well for himself.

"You know," he said, "you really get to know a man in his cups. Saying 'Prost' once together is better than the so-called bushel of salt.[11] Don't you think so?" and he turned to Sturm.

---

11. From an old expression: "Den Freund zu erkennen, musst du erst einen Scheffel Salz mit ihm gegessen haben," or, literally, "In order to truly recognize a friend, you have to have first eaten a bushel of salt with him." In other words, time is necessary—a stipulation the Engineer rejects.

"Certainly. I've spent a great deal of time making such observations—in others, in animals, and in myself."

"In animals?"

"In animals. I was a zoologist, you see. Let's say you give a hen alcohol. It will crow, spring around, and flap its wings like mad. In addition to the stimulation of the entire organism, that's primarily the result of the relaxation of the inhibitory elements of the ganglia.

"That's a special characteristic of alcohol intoxication. Everyone can witness it in himself. At least a hundred times a day, a man experiences desires that emerge fleetingly from the depths of his brain and pass away again. He feels like roaring with laughter for no reason, pounding the table with his fist, or suddenly engaging another person by saying coarse or loving things to him. Sometimes, on the other hand, he has the urge to make faces, touch his tongue to one's nose, or whistle a bizarre tune. He might even give way to these impulses, if he is alone in one's room. In the presence of others, however, he hides these desires, which incessantly press for expression, under the mask of convention.

"These inhibitions disappear under the influence of alcohol, where a man shows himself as he is underneath. Of course, he doesn't reveal his essential being, as the essential being of a man is something about which one can form no clearer an idea than one can of a thing in and of itself. But under the influence, personalities lose their exterior shell and can meld more easily with one another. Feelings connect directly—they are no longer divided by qualities like politeness, deliberation, shyness, and reserve. A man claps his companion amiably on the shoulder, if he wants to, or grabs her by the waist, if she's a girl. He pours his heart out. He lets feelings flow. He feels: Only in intoxication, only in this moment, which he wishes to prolong, is life worth something."

This debate seemed of little interest to the Engineer. He stabbed his bayonet indifferently into the fire and murmured: "I haven't spent too much time up to this point worrying about the thing in and of itself."

"I can only congratulate you on that," replied Sturm. "It's a German national vice, to seek so vigorously what's behind things that the things themselves stop being real. These days men who can throw hand grenades farther than 60 meters are more valuable to us."

"Those might be the same ones who know their way around a good bottle," threw in Döhring, who so far had been silent.

"That only confirms what I just said. For men who are driven now and then to fly beyond their inhibitions on the wings of intoxication, there's no great difference between the onslaught of an attack and the feeling of excitement in the midst of drunken company. The intensification of living, the racing circulation of the blood, the sudden changes in mood, the explosion of thoughts in the brain—that is the form of being, that manifests itself in them." — — —

"You spoke this afternoon, though, during our so suddenly interrupted conversation, about some lines you had written about men at war. How about reading us something from that? The time is moving damned slowly. Lieutenant von Horn's eyes are already closing."

"I don't object, although it seems I can't count on the most attentive audience. At any rate, this evening will stay with me. It's so typical for this war. Perhaps, if I come through it, I'll try to write a Decameron of the dugouts: ten old warriors, who crouch around a fire as we do here, and relate their experiences."

He pulled a thin notebook out of the table's clutter, which had been added to by fragments of brick from the ceiling, adjusted the carbide lamp, and began to read:

6

"Tonight, as on every evening when dusk settled on the crooked lanes of the old city, his narrow, barracks-like room had become unbearable to Ensign Kiel. In long years of subterranean warfare, he had become used to living intensely at this hour. The clatter of cooking pots and the cold, silver shine of the first flare rose up in him as, freed of his tight-fitting uniform, he strolled past the rows of gray buildings, in which small soldiers' taverns opened their red eyes and in whose dark corners swarms of children caroused at late play.

"Each time he did so, his inherited adventurers' blood, whose like dimly shone forth from ancient city chronicles, became peculiarly attuned to the bright, harmonious refrains that had for centuries washed over these same gray, bent gables. And so, moved to remarkably melancholic and dark thoughts by the contrast between time and the passing generations and the fleeting life of the individual, he often leaned over the railings of old bridges and stared into the dirty water of the river, which spilled past eroded walls under the light evening mist. He transposed himself into long-gone days, when misery crept into the houses through poisonous vapors, pestilence weighed down a prostrate population, and plague-laborers strode with crude jokes through the alleys in order to load corpses taken from anxious survivors onto their carts.

"His carriage altered when he neared the center of the city. He held himself straighter, his lightweight, dark coat fluttering around him, his sharp, haggard face sharply underlined by a white collar. With the deep, awakening inhalations of a beginning intoxication, he took in the noise of the turbulent city center like a wild beast that leaves its lair in order to seek his prey. Just as at this hour in previous days adventure had driven him over the clicking barbed wire into the desolate no-man's-land, now an urge toward experience chased him into the surging breakers of the big city at night. As he was intelligent, the periodic intoxication of the evenings occasioned some reluctance in him, yet there was too much self-assurance and brutality in him for him to perceive that a higher force drove him to these nightly outings. He took the hunt for women as something necessary for the body, discomfort as the trough in the wave of intoxication, and, precisely because he lived so intensely, thought no further about his existence.

"Slowly, alertly, he let himself be carried along by the stream of scrubbed-clean people. His sharp glance, trained in noting what was essential, engaged the passersby as with the exchange of pistol fire, penetrated them, and demanded an answer to his question. Often a woman's mouth shaped itself into a smile as a result of a lightning-fast calculation. This feel of many eyes upon him kept him going, made merely walking a pleasure, drove him proudly through the dense emanation of lascivious thoughts and wishes. Every step seemed to him to open a new wellspring, every paving stone the field of a great game of chance, every woman the potential bearer of something unexpected, long sought after.

"Gradually this feeling condensed into intoxication, demanded expression. He felt the pressing need to empty the overflow of his energy into some kind of vessel, to smash its crest onto some woman. All of those he saw here seemed unsuitable. The path to them led through cafés, wine bars, dark alleys; they demanded courtship, development, a short novel— a dime novel, as it were, but a novel nonetheless. They wanted to listen, to talk, and to be understood as personalities exactly then, when he sought to surrender his. These women broke the most natural thing in the world down into the small change of bourgeois convention. The evening would roll itself out like a kitschy, oft-seen film. Clichés danced in his brain. 'What do you think of me?' Country boys who landed in the city might have found the role of the conqueror wonderfully worldly, but his manhood rebelled against it. He thought of night patrols after short, intense bursts of fire, brutal attacks, steel helmets, hand grenades. Hardly five minutes, and one had trampled the enemy. After years of goal-oriented, concentrated living, his eroticism demanded a manlier stamp, a return to elemental simplicity. Just as he had learned to prefer alcohol in its strong, unwatered form, so he needed to enjoy every experience as an all-out assault on a goal.

"Following a sudden decision, he turned into a side street, where love proffered itself in a freer, more direct form. The exterior of the restless, silk-clad streetwalkers was already designed to captivate the excited senses, with garish colors, strangely shaped hats, stockings whose weave only let the skin burst forth more nakedly, artificial fragrances, rustling undergarments. All of these girls seemed to him like strange flowers, false blossoms, which attempted to lure swarms of pollinating insects through scent and color. Their advertisement-like self-presentation, their billboard-like conspicuousness, pleased him. The libido was on frank display here. He felt like an Asiatic despot, rendered homage by a display of barbarian pageantry. All of it was on show only to honor him, to honor manhood.

"One girl walking by caught his eye. Her head and face were a mask, but they were carried by a wonderful body. The forms flowed supply together, gave her gait the fullness of suppressed power seen in great predators. He spoke to her and left with her.

"In the middle of the night he awoke. After collecting his thoughts he turned on the light. He stared at her face. The closed eyes enhanced the masklike quality that her profession had stamped there after thousands of nights. The eternal lust of the big city had chiseled a smile in her features, half smug, half challenging—a frozen, entombed grimace that now inundated the observer with waves of loathing.

"Suddenly, out of some dark sensation of contrast, the image of a half-forgotten figure emerged: a girl whom he had loved with an intensity inconceivable to him now, although in boyish bashfulness he had never exchanged a word with her. A garden in summer, loose, light clothing, a lock of hair that always fell in her face—how lovely that all was! And then the war, the 'those-who-are-about-to-die' mood, scrubbed away the tender portrait with a rough hand, placing glaring lights next to the black shadows. It showed its terrible influence everywhere—a relapse into barbarism, into a web of medieval passions. Only sometimes, in hours of weariness, the longing for tender, lyrical sensation emerged as a fata morgana from the wreckage of a shattered culture.

"Quietly he rose, dressed himself, took the key from the night table, and left the house."

When Sturm closed the notebook and looked up, he saw that the Engineer was fast asleep. Döhring, who seemed to have listened attentively, thanked him and suggested that they take a short walk through the trenches in order to check in with the sentries and then resume the reading. They made themselves ready and went out. The night had become cool and still; the morning announced itself with a fresh, dew-laden breeze that refreshed the overtired nerves. From the shadows of a mighty traverse a figure detached itself, laid a hand on its steel helmet, and reported, "Sector of the third platoon. Everything in order." It was Hugershoff.

The three officers shook hands and began a whispered conversation. It hardly seemed possible that there would be an attack—the night was so quiet. At any rate, it would be best to keep the state of alarm in effect until daybreak. While they still spoke, a sergeant appeared and relieved Hugershoff. "Come along with us," said Döhring. "We still have some grog, and Sturm is going to read to us until dawn. Then we can lie down with a good conscience and sleep until noon." They went back and found the Engineer still in the same position. They lifted him carefully from the chair and laid him on the bed without awakening him. Hugershoff took the free place; Sturm opened the notebook anew and read:

7

"Falk had no friends. Acquaintances, whom his studies, cafés, and his literary efforts wafted from time to time into his orbit, tended soon to become nothing more to him than names and the necessity of a quick greeting. To his landlady he was someone for whom each morning books, linens, and cigarette butts needed to be tidied up and very frequently a double breakfast had to be delivered. Measured by bourgeois standards, he was a washout and the failed hope of pitiable parents.

"In his own mind, too, he counted for little, and saw precisely in that the reason for his lack of success. He knew that eyes should be lightning, not mirror, appearance must be attack, and speech assault, in order to impress people. Whatever value one might possess, only one's appearance could penetrate their consciousness. He admired people who knew the trick of this as if they were magicians who knew how to conjure up flowers and butterflies out of thin air. From time to time he felt himself consumed with deep bitterness when others heedlessly passed him by. At those times he felt his soul to be a dark, isolated country, rich in gold and rare things, and ringed by gloomy ancient forests. If he made the attempt, though, to penetrate the thicket, his treasures slipped away from him along the way, and he brought only laughter or a colorless Nothing to light.

"After experiences like this, which transpired on street corners and in the most ordinary situations without anyone else realizing it, he withdrew from all contact for days. Smoking cigarettes, he lay on the sofa in his apartment, reading or staring blankly at the ceiling. He loved Gogol, Dostoevsky, and Balzac, writers who stalked the human soul like hunters after elusive prey and who, by the glow of pit lights, penetrated the deepest shafts in order to enjoy the rush of the discoverer amidst crystals and jagged primeval rocks. Reading was more to him than empathy and the delight in the play of another's thoughts; it was a form of living to him, wholly spiritual, which transported him effortlessly to all manner of passion and bliss. These great writers made succinct and meaningful formulas out of a tangle of equations, forged in the fire of their power true life, in its clear and eternal form, out of inconsistencies, emptiness, and superfluities. Characters emerged, honed by their minds, suffused with the glow of their hearts, and revealed the most hidden things, transparent as glass circled by a battery of spotlights. From the outside one could see blood spurt red through their veins, nerve endings twitch from the interplay of the will, a thousand arc lamps rattle in the eddying energy of their brains. Exuberance and the dammed-up desire to rush madly past borders and obstacles became comprehensible before they flamed up into the magnificent or subsided into the terrible. One fought with heroes, betrayed with traitors, and murdered with murderers and, bewitched by their spell, as forced to recognize battle, betrayal, and murder as inner necessities. And above it all like the sun stood the writer, the artist, shedding rays of light on the proceedings and causing it to turn around his axis in a predetermined arc. He was the blessed one, a consciously closed element in the great circuit, an eye of God. Hate felled one figure, love another; one killed an old woman without knowing why: In the writer everything and everyone found redemption and understanding. He was the great consciousness of mankind, an electrical charge over the wasteland of hearts. In him his age was crystallized, the personal found eternal value. He was the dazzling foam at the breaking crest of a dark wave that glided in the sea of eternity. — — —

"Falk gladly lost himself in such thoughts. Being sensitive, he often felt the urge to express himself, only to founder each time on the form. If he stared for an hour at an empty page, feather in hand, he was that much more despondent at his lack of fecundity, for he knew that he had good material in him. Just as in his interactions with people, the seed within him lay in so hard a shell that it spoiled in the darkness. At such times it was a relief to him to imagine the writerly as something without boundaries, something existing in all things living—as a world-ether, in which the stars of mankind swung up and down. So he perceived his own feelings in those of others and sensed that the glow that swelled in him like the hidden fire in the bowels of a ship must find its expression somewhere, at last. What did it matter if a tree shed ten thousand seeds in the fall? If only one grew, didn't the ten thousand hopes bloom in fulfillment?

"From time to time, however, the individual in him rebelled against this ecstatic-submissive flight into the cosmic. There must be some reason that the universal splintered into countless elements. And if he were only the smallest splinter, he wanted fulfillment, wanted to gather experience before he disappeared again. At those moments he threw aside his books and papers and plunged into the vortex of the city.

"Among all the connections that melded the multiplicity of sounds, lights, and bright tatters into a single mass, he was attuned to one: the sexual. That city love, which burned on the paving stones every evening in a muted red glow, was the one way out and the means by which he hoped to outrun himself. For him there was no path that meandered its way through a bright and free countryside—only one that wound nightly from one bitter station of recognition to the next. He often envied the animals that swam past him in pairs in the stream of the streets. The same clothing, the same faces, the same conversations, the same feelings. Forming them ever more exactly, ever more to type, time and conditions gave rise to these creatures that danced around the lights like a swarm of glistening insects.

"Of course, the hairy man of the Steppes, the ravening hunter, had loved more strongly, crouching in his cave before a bright fire and splintering marrow bones with his mighty bite. Mere shepherds lived more simply and attractively, their lives flowing melodically between gentle animals and blue skies. Free and conscious of good laws, the people of classical cultures strode amidst naked statues. Asia lay very far away. Even Louis XIV would have been kitschified or made the subject of a film if he still lived. A Casanova would at most have found space in the legal columns of the newspapers.

"There was no more nature, no art, no great line, nor even any style: Everything that went by those names now was diminishment and self-deception. Since the emergence of the machine, everything had been razed flat by buzzing flywheels. Like a furious plague, the mechanization of men had transformed Europe into a desert; tomorrow, in the furthest village of the Congo, trembling films on screens would transform values, would transpose the meeting of the sexes from nightly palavers accompanied by the droning of drums to fashionable dance halls. Just as man gradually hunted down the last great, colorful animals or put them on display behind bars, so he gradually destroyed everything left that was born out of hot blood.

"And yet: He envied the men of the era. If they were nothing more than surface, creatures of master tailors and differentiated in their exteriors only through assets in the most literal sense, they were at the same time so easily made content. If they had money and health, they spent, earned, and were happy. Certainly they were happier than he was—the writer who could find no words. All this brooding, this urge toward recognition, was a fissure in the composition of the world, a laughable attempt to penetrate the depths of something whose surface was perhaps its entire meaning.

"Sometimes he wished to be a simple animal, a plant, or some kind of life, not differentiated in the least. He hated the idea of an evolution whose ever more finely organized creatures also had to experience every torture endlessly augmented.

"Of course, the more variously and intricately a creature sank its roots into the earth, the more various and strange its intoxications became. But that was as nothing against the growing force of depression. Falk had experienced it often in himself. Not least in the realm of love.

"He had once found in a philosopher the following sentence: 'The kind and degree of a man's sexuality reaches into the utmost pinnacle of his spirit.' He had thought a long time about this, and it seemed to him that one could here, as in most cases, argue the opposite. In his case, the restless striving of the spirit, the devouring of values without being satisfied, the dogged fury to lose oneself in the multiplicity of things, were far more motivating than mere bodily lust. For this much he was sure of: What drove him to women was not pleasure, but a wound that burned deep down.

"The best time was when, searching, he strode through the city hung with lights. When shops and offices emptied, and metal grates were rolled down in front of store windows, the veins of the city were swept suddenly through with a shot of female blood. Blondes and brunettes, slenderness, and laughter conjured dreams of fulfillment and promise in his brain. Each one had her own tone, knew how to put some puzzle on display that tempted one to investigate. Clothing, haircut, rhythm of movement, smile, glance, the play of lines on the face—all of that called forth that particular admixture of concealment and revelation, a hint of rare pleasures, that always drove him to new expeditions. Sometimes the frustration of limitations shot through him here—he wanted to embrace them all, rob them of their secrets, and know them all.

"If these feelings of excitement should send him running to one of them in particular, his experience was the same every time, whether it played out at a table of one of the giant beer halls, behind the plush red curtains of a wine bar, in a color-splashed variety show, on a forest path, or at the seaside docks. Every time, conversation flowed back and forth in which he, casual and a bit melancholy, made a sympathetic and insignificant impression. He listened to stories and asked about trifles—working hours, breaks, books, friends, lovers—invented some situation, event, and asked for her judgment. Sometimes he contradicted in order to test the strength of her resistance; sometimes he agreed with her in order to incite her to further exposure through retreat.

"In this way he pieced together a spiritual portrait of the other's personality, and all of these portraits were nauseatingly similar. While he erected these edifices, guessing at the missing stroke in the flow of the line, here and there painstakingly painting in details of milieu or temperament, the other that he had constructed beforehand every time—the ideal edifice—imperceptibly faded away. Nothing remained but an experience. And it became ever more certain to him that experience meant disappointment and life at most was the sum of experiences of disappointment.

"After he had already taken possession of, recognized, and despised everything essential, what could mere physical penetration offer? It was all of pleasure and all of torture compressed in a single moment. It was, in one breathless deed, the embodiment of hate and love, promise and recognition, deception and self-deception, flight and fall. It was the Bestial, from which everything emanated and into which everything issued. The rest was loathing.

"There were hours when he jeered at himself for seeking the eternal One in so many. No more would these custodians of the great mysterium tempt him to renewed idol worship through their many priestly arts. Quiet and stolid, he would plant himself before their altars and heartily consume the mysterious holy of holies as his daily bread: conversion to the bourgeois, the limited—exams, position, marriage, a blond happiness, and smooth sailing ahead. If he made the attempt, however, to find a bridge into that landscape of clear horizons by means of a longer connection, a relationship, he had to admit the impossibility of it every time. He had never yet stuck it out longer than three days without losing himself in an irritable, dissatisfied mood.

"No, it was surely better to destroy the last vestiges of the spiritual and sentimental with a firm hand. In the evenings he sat over viscous beer in the vaulted cellar of a small, ancient brewery where students had sat together for centuries. This beer hall lay in a narrow, winding lane that only otherwise sheltered brothels, whose pointed gables met high above. And so the light of the stars seeped only weakly onto the round cobblestones; lanterns in rusty cages flickered in the wind. When it rained, silent figures in long coats scurried by in order to disappear into different doors. Shadows swayed up and down and veiled the corners in spooky unreality. From somewhere a drunken monologue revolved around three nonsense words; a brawl sprang up from grumbling and squalling in the night.

"The Middle Ages had become entangled here and rested in timelessness, while quite close by the evening raced through lights in roaring cataracts.

"On the oak benches against the walls of the beer cellar sat people who knew how to keep up the tone—men and a few women. A brutality of historic proportions was the order of the day. Massive tankards were emptied; sharply spiced sausages, brought by a slattern from the kitchen still sizzling in the pan, were devoured in great quantities. Tobacco smoke, the crashing impact of the dice cups, the onslaught of jokes, and the thunder of laughter packed the cave to the last corner full of noise and fumes. Glasses of schnapps were kept track of with matchsticks and the sums owed written with chalk on the tables. The high point was heralded each time by the appearance of a crooked old man who put a zither on the table and began to rasp out strange songs.

"Then everything was in an uproar: Everyone screamed, roared, laughed, became the center of people, sounds, and lights that the intoxication spun around in frantic circles. Dissolving, they radiated extreme emotions, which congregated around light and dark poles. Embraces wrenched people together; pacts of brotherhood were sealed. Were they less meaningful for the fact that they would be forgotten tomorrow? One man, who sat quietly at the table, was suddenly thrashed and thrust out into the night without hat or coat. He had aroused aversion through his very existence. That was enough, was a sacrilege against feeling. Feeling was everything. Why? Because one felt it. One man wept—his whole world melted away in sadness. A girl became ill and was dragged behind the bar. In one corner stood a group who continuously on command threw back their heads in order to let shots of schnapps run down their throats. One man gave a speech—inspirational, brilliant, urged on by the pressure of his thoughts—and was catapulted to the peak of ecstasy. What did it matter that no one listened? Realities had lost their meaning; a thousand possibilities rolled past, dazzling and weightless, and were grasped while still in embryo. Ideas flamed up into glowing primeval mists of intoxication, so fine and fluid that they effortlessly penetrated everything. Hearts beat against ribs like red beasts of prey against the bars of a cage and forced ever stronger, ever hotter waves of blood into brains—these brains that otherwise were mired, cold and bloodless, in the comprehensible. And so emerged the hidden powers of the blood to bring about the rebirth of conditions that lay already far in the twilight past. The undivided, the origin, was brought to life and cried for release, for a pure and wild deed. That was a beautiful, powerful feeling, a rediscovery of the self amidst the torturous nonsense of reason. Finally the atmosphere thickened to the point that, like a blast of gunpowder, it forced everyone through a narrow passageway into the open air. There the human payload shattered in laughter and noise and, like an army of plunderers, dispersed into the surrounding houses.

"With a certain pleasure, Falk noted from time to time that he was devolving—he was developing along cruder but simpler lines. At first he had walked like a cursed prince through the palaces of evil, had imagined his destiny and individuality there, and from the idea that he was lost among the lost, had searched among the debris for veins of gold and diamond splinters. He had soon discarded these ideas as the passion of romantic store clerks, already exhausted in thousands of cheap novels. He set his sights lower, started giving current coinage, and finally got his money's worth. He was soon capable of giving his desires clear names and of emanating the self-confidence and matter-of-factness of a carpenter's apprentice at the end of the week.

"One evening Falk sat in the streetcar, seeking his usual goal. He was reading, for he loved to absorb fragments of books on short trips, in cafés, and during dinner, framing spiritual images with noise, music, and crowds. This brought on strange moods: He was in India, in Rome in the time of the caesars, in a philosophical system and at the same time in the burning heart of the big city, so that in the rapid change of spaces, times, and ideas, the moment lost its obtrusiveness. This state, which would lose its finest attributes if one tried to fix it too closely, gave Falk the feeling of having nimbly extracted himself from rule-boundedness, from constriction.

"When he looked up one time, a girl sat opposite him with the same book in her hand as his. It was Hippolyte Taine's *Balzac*, so the coincidence wasn't exactly ordinary; a smile hinted at it, and a conversation confirmed it. Falk invited this girl, whom he took for a student or an academic, to share the evening with him. His invitation was accepted.

"The usual bottle of wine beforehand, he thought, as they sat, now the thing would play out until the cigarette afterward. Cheers, hands examined, a ring, first name, please no, well then. He leaned back in the worn sofa and threw the first coin into the conversation machine.

"Yet he soon lost this nonchalance, leaned forward, sharpened his gaze, and weighed each sentence carefully before he uttered it. He spied resistance, display, panache in her wrist. But that wasn't it—he saw comprehension. Already with the first exchange of sounds he felt it surge back to him, stimulating, electric, unanticipated. He felt himself channeled into a strange current, diverted into a fluid and mobile element whose existence had been completely hidden to him beforehand. An easy cheerfulness that lay far away in his boyhood lifted him over all obstacles that would otherwise have barred his way.

"Because the nearness of other people bothered him, he soon made the suggestion that they seek his apartment—a suggestion that was accepted with such blitheness that he was happily astonished. On the way there she hung lightly on his arm, so lightly that he felt her gait next to him as something unreal but also full of life.

"The room was warm and dark. Falk opened the door of the glowing oven, from which streamed a dull redness. It was like a furnace in a foggy landscape; here and there a sharper line suggested a chair, table, or book. Only a cloud of smoke from Falk's cigarette swam clearly above the murk as something delineated and distinct.

"Falk took his companion's coat and hat and invited her to have a seat. She thanked him.

"'I like it here. There's atmosphere in the shimmer of red that hangs over your room. Red is my favorite color. It's a shout, a challenge, something unconditional.'

"'That's true. It compels us to look into the fire and awakens strange, faraway memories. There's something alluring and wild in it. A girl once told me that she owned a hat in the shape of a large red disk and that she never walked the street in it without being propositioned by men. I saw men in the war…'

"'You've seen blood? You seem young yet.'

"'I was a boy who could barely heft a gun when I saw my first battle. We had marched all night, dull and overtired, toward a storm that hung red on the horizon. In the morning we strode through a village in which a strange, hurried existence persisted. A horse with bulging, wild eyes raced, stirrups clanking, through the streets. Somewhere a door was being broken down. Two people carried by a third, his arms dragging along the ground. Very nearby, in gardens and behind houses, there was a crashing sound as if iron barrels were being tossed around. We walked as if in a dream. Behind the village the fields were deserted; only a few corpses lay along the road.

"'This can't be real, I thought, and felt at the same time a detached curiosity at how it would all turn out. We halted behind a clump of woods; a sharp voice rapped out a few sentences whose meaning we didn't comprehend. Then we crossed the woods in small detachments. On the far side we saw small earth entrenchments, out of which we were being shot at. We ran, threw ourselves to the ground, fired, and sprang up again.

"'The air near our skulls was rent by cracking and popping sounds. This isn't right, this isn't right, roared repeatedly in my ears; I might well have been screaming it myself. I let myself fall and lay behind a bush; the shells swirled around like a swarm of hornets. I had hardly lain down when a blow knocked my helmet off of my head. I touched my head with my hand and it came away warm and moist. When I looked down, it was covered in blood. I wiped my face; blood burned in my eyes and flowed in my mouth, hot and bland.

"'I stood up. The landscape was strangely altered. A bloody sun circled over vermillion fields. Screams, shots, and thoughts were all bathed in red. Ahead near the entrenchments red figures danced in confusion. A torrential wave gripped me and propelled me with irresistible force. I raced like a screaming devil over the ground and pitched headfirst into the carnage. My rifle was loaded, but I carried it like a club and struck out around me, without distinguishing between friend and foe, until I fell to the ground exhausted from loss of blood.

"'I awoke in a white bed and could soon stand. Beforehand I had often thought that battle would make me serious and manly, but as I strode through lonesome streets in my hospital gown, I could feel only the frailty of the invalid. The immensity had not touched me; it remained something inscrutable which had appeared like a fiery isle and then sunk away again. Only a certain anxiety remained, a feeling of unconsciously harboring immeasurable powers—the feeling that one has in a much reduced measure when, awaking the morning after a senseless debauch, one realizes one has lived many hours in great intensity though far from consciously.'

"'Did you feel remorse or at least revulsion?'

"'I couldn't say. More like horror and amazement and the certainty that I had never been so strong, so determined. I had killed—that couldn't be denied—and not in self-defense, but in attack. I also had to admit that all of the nationalistic and heroic ideals that had seemed to be the driving forces beforehand evaporated before this passion like drops of water on a red-hot iron plate.

"'When I spoke with others about it, I noticed how little at home with themselves people are, essentially. Some sought to sanctify it, some to excuse it; still others condemned it. To all of them, though, it seemed that it was not their experience of the thing, but what they thought of it afterward, that was essential. What they related was not at all what they had experienced; it came from…'"

8

When Sturm had read to this point, Hugershoff suddenly grabbed him by the arm: "Quiet! Didn't someone just yell outside?" They listened. Yes, there! The long-drawn-out cry of a nearby guard rang out, remarkably shrill and piercing: "Look out, mortar!!"

A whooshing and fluttering sound followed, ending in a massive explosion. The cellar swayed; its walls cracked at every joint. A heavy mortar shell seemed to have hit it directly. The lamp was extinguished, the fire burnt down. The voice of the Engineer issued from a corner: "Light, by God, light!" From the staircase Kettler cried out: "Help me, Lieutenant, I'm buried! Air! Air!"

The tumult of the scene was heightened by a ceaseless series of detonations that made the cellar quake like a ship in a hurricane. The momentary pauses between the heavy impacts were filled with the rattle of rifle fire. It was undeniable: the attack had begun.

Sturm finally managed to find the matches in the midst of the confusion. He struck one and saw that the lamp had disappeared. Without hesitating, he grabbed the notebook he had been reading from, ripped a few pages out, and set them on fire. He let the burning leaves fall to the ground as the Engineer ripped apart books and pictures in order to keep the fire going.

When the inhabitants of the cellar, who had hastily armed themselves, were ready to charge outside, they encountered another obstacle: The stairs were blocked from floor to ceiling by large pieces of rubble. The first mortar shell must have fallen directly on top of the stairs.

"Through the light shaft," cried the Engineer, whose voice had regained its quiet, clear tone. Döhring ripped the cardboard away so that the light of dawn fell through the window into the room. The Engineer climbed on the table, raised his arms above his head, and forced his body through the narrow shaft while Döhring supported him from beneath. They handed him a rifle, and then he helped Hugershoff and Döhring through. Sturm wanted to follow them, but the thought of Kettler pulled him back. He set about tearing away the rubble that had blocked his burrow. He had soon cleared the opening and succeeded in grabbing Kettler by the collar and hauling him out. He left the body, which showed no signs of life, lying on the stones and hurried out after the others.

When he emerged he found the others already engaged in battle. The mortar barrage had fallen silent, but in its place was a wall of artillery fire. Döhring and Horn lay on the front wall of a huge shell crater and fired. Hugershoff lay on the ground; he seemed to be dead or at least seriously wounded. When Sturm sprang into the crater, the Engineer turned around and looked at him with a wild expression on his face. A shell had grazed his forehead; blood streamed from a deep furrow below his hairline. He pulled his rifle back and used his right hand to rub clean the gunsight while he wiped blood from his eyes with the left. Sturm clapped Döhring on the shoulder: "What is it?"

"The English are in the trench."

It was undeniable. From up ahead rang out the dull, un-mistakable burst of hand grenades. From time to time a clay-colored figure appeared above the rim of the trench, made a throwing motion, and then disappeared again. Sturm raised his rifle and fired. The goal was to home in on the tar-get as fast as lightning and then vanish. And so the three men lay next to one another and fired until heat waves shimmered above their barrels. Gradually it became still. Sturm bent down to Hugershoff in order to bind his wounds; after one look at his waxen yellow face, however, he threw the pack of bandages aside.

Döhring looked at his watch. "The trench garrison seems to have had it. Horn, we have to try to get your Engineer company..."

A machine gun that suddenly started up from the left flank ripped the words from his mouth. Bullets combed the area beyond the crater or burst at its rim. Horn took a second hit that cost him a piece of his shoulder and a hand-sized tear in his uniform. Things looked grim. The enemy appeared to have penetrated deeply on the left into the communications trenches. The three battle comrades crouched together on the floor of the crater; it was impossible to raise their heads in the midst of the barrage. Sturm looked from one to the other; he had a strange feeling of detachment. It felt to him as if he were watching a play. Döhring was very pale; he gripped the butt of his pistol firmly but with a light trembling. The Engineer's calmness was remarkable. He took his field canteen from a clasp at his waist, uncorked it, drained it, and threw it aside: "It's a shame to leave any undrunk."

Now events unfolded very rapidly. The storm of shells broke off suddenly. When the three men raised themselves, they saw an English advance troop standing before them. "You are pris-oners," a voice called out. Sturm looked rigidly at the Engineer's face. It was like a flame, white and burnt through. Then came the answer: "No, sir," accompanied by a pistol shot.

A salvo of hand grenades and rifle shots rang out. The figures vanished in a cloud of fire, spraying earth, and whitish fumes. When the haze lifted, only Sturm still stood. He raised his pistol one last time, and then a blow to the left side of his chest robbed him of sight and hearing.

His last feeling was of sinking into the eddy of an ancient melody.

Also from Telos Press Publishing

Eumeswil
Ernst Jünger

The Forest Passage
Ernst Jünger

On Pain
Ernst Jünger

The Adventurous Heart: Figures and Capriccios
Ernst Jünger

Theory of the Partisan
Carl Schmitt

The Nomos *of the Earth*
in the International Law of the Jus Publicum Europaeum
Carl Schmitt

Hamlet or Hecuba:
The Intrusion of the Time into the Play
Carl Schmitt

Germany and Iran
From the Aryan Axis to the Nuclear Threshold
Matthias Küntzel

The New Class Conflict
Joel Kotkin

Confronting the Crisis: Writings of Paul Piccone
Paul Piccone

A Journal of No Illusions:
Telos, *Paul Piccone, and the Americanization of Critical Theory*
Timothy W. Luke and Ben Agger, eds.

Praise for Ernst Jünger's *Sturm*

"An unblinking account of a culture in twilight, this novella recasts central themes of Ernst Jünger's chronicles of the Great War: the unrelenting test of human perdurance under new technologies of annihilation; the naturalist's precise aesthetic of life teeming amid martial insanity; and, a new note, the harrowing free fall of civilian life into erotic aimlessness and inebriated despair, for which only art serves for an antidote. In Alexis Walker's carefully wrought translation, *Sturm* will be a welcome surprise to Jünger's veteran readers, and an ideal introduction for those who are curious to know more than his name."

> —**Thomas Nevin**, author of *Ernst Jünger and Germany: Into the Abyss, 1914–1945*

"Had Stephen Crane's Henry Fleming been born in 1895 Germany, his story might very well have read like the eponymous protagonist's of Ernst Jünger's *Sturm*. In a fascinating novella in turn meditative and wrenchingly physical, Jünger stages a drama of one man's ideas about himself, as told through a narration conflicted about its own subject."

> —**Alex Vernon**, James and Emily Bost Odyssey Professor of English, Hendrix College

"*Sturm* is a subtle novella about an intellectual in the trenches who sees the age of industrial-scale war as deeply dehumanizing, yet recognizes that this war has given him a sense of identity, and of community with others, that no peacetime experience could match.... Jünger is a remarkable writer. In this novella he comes across as a romantic with a loathing of modernity, especially as characterized by the overbearing state. The book is grim, and deeply pessimistic—but exceptionally interesting, and well worth reading."

> —**George Simmers**, *Great War Fiction* blog